J R ECKEL

NOMOGRAPHY

NOMOGRAPHY

BY A. S. LEVENS, M.S., C.E.

Associate Professor of Mechanical Engineering
University of California, Berkeley, California

JOHN WILEY & SONS, INC., NEW YORK
CHAPMAN & HALL, LTD., LONDON

PRINTED IN THE UNITED STATES OF AMERICA

PREFACE

In science and technology, nomograms are recognized for ease of operation and for the time saved in the repeated solution of mathematical formulas. The type of nomogram known as the alignment chart has won much favor during the past two decades. Engineers and scientists should be trained sufficiently to understand the mathematical theory and design of nomograms. The material presented in this book is intended to provide a good working knowledge of the fundamental principles.

Emphasis is placed upon the "geometric method" employed in the development of the theory for the design of alignment charts involving equations of three or more variables. Simple equations are solved by alignment charts consisting of straight-line scales, whereas more involved equations may necessitate the use of "grids," curved scales, and combinations of Cartesian co-ordinate charts with alignment charts.

Once the theory is well understood, practical short-cuts are presented to reduce the time required to design a chart. Examples are given in the chapter "Practical Short-Cuts."

The chapter on the use of determinants serves as an introduction to the "method of determinants" which has been well developed by such writers as d'Ocagne, Soreau, Hewes and Seward, and Allcock and Jones.

The appendix contains practical examples of alignment charts used in the fields of engineering, production, and statistics.

This book is an outgrowth of nomography courses offered for many years at both the University of Minnesota and the University of California. At present, one-semester, two-unit, elective courses are open for seniors in engineering, physics, chemistry, business administration, and education. Scientists and practicing engineers will find no difficulty in handling the material in this book, if they have not forgotten the elements of algebra and plane geometry and the use of logarithms.

For those who may develop a keen desire to pursue further study in the fascinating field of Nomography the selected bibliography will provide adequate reference material.

v

The author is indebted to both Emeritus Professor W. H. Kirchner, formerly head of the Department of Drawing and Descriptive Geometry, and Emeritus Professor W. E. Brooke, formerly head of the Department of Mathematics and Mechanics, at the University of Minnesota, for their guidance and encouragement during the early years of training and experience. Acknowledgments are due undergraduate and graduate students of the author's classes in Nomography, especially Russell M. Carlson, of the Engineering Department, Chance Vought Aircraft Division of United Aircraft Corporation, and colleagues of the Department of Engineering, University of California, for many valuable suggestions. The writer is grateful to Professors B. F. Raber and F. W. Hutchinson of the University of California, authors of "Refrigeration and Air Conditioning Engineering"; the Crane Company; Consolidated Vultee Aircraft Corporation; Crobalt, Inc.; Product Engineering; and Federal Telephone and Radio Corporation for permission to reproduce certain nomograms.

A. S. LEVENS

University of California
Berkeley, California
August, 1947

CONTENTS

Chapter One

INTRODUCTION

Pictorial representation has proved to be an effective method in conveying technical and semi-technical information to business and professional persons, to production personnel, to engineers, and to scientists.

Our daily newspapers, business magazines, company publications, technical papers, etc., invariably present graphs and charts which quickly and painlessly disclose information that would otherwise require lengthy descriptions if presented by the printed word. Figures 1, 2, and 3 are typical of such charts.

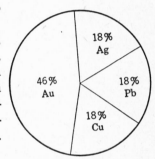

FIG. 1. Pie Chart.

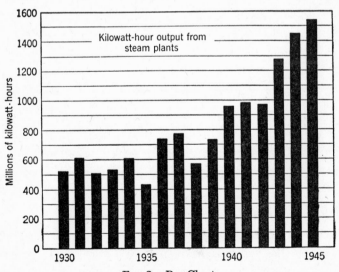

FIG. 2. Bar Chart.

1

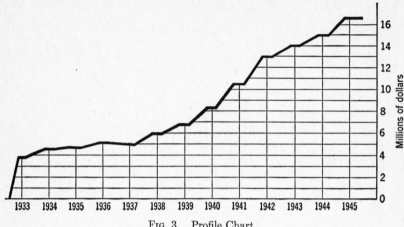

FIG. 3.   Profile Chart.

Those engaged in technical work frequently employ the Cartesian co-ordinate system for the representation of the relationship between two or more variables. For example, the straight line $y = -2x + 7$ is represented graphically by Figure 4. If $x = 2$, the value of y may be determined by following the arrows shown in the figure, which yields $y = 3$

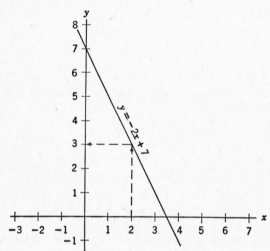

FIG. 4.   Cartesian Co-ordinate Representation of the Equation, $y = -2x + 7$. *Example*: When $x = 2$, $y = 3$.

Several equations of the form $y = mx + b$ can, of course, be shown on one set of axes. For example, the equations

$$y = -2x + 1 \tag{1}$$

$$y = -2x + 2 \tag{2}$$

$$y = -2x + 3 \tag{3}$$

$$y = -2x + 5 \tag{4}$$

$$y = -2x - 4 \tag{5}$$

will appear as a family of parallel lines.   (See Figure 5.)

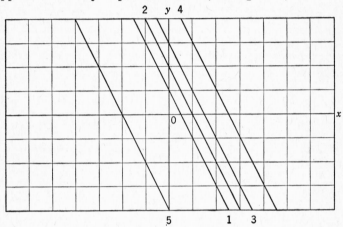

FIG. 5.   Family of Parallel Lines.   (1) $y = -2x + 1$.   (2) $y = -2x + 2$.   (3) $y = -2x + 3$.   (4) $y = -2x + 5$.   (5) $y = -2x - 4$.

An equation of the form $f_1(u) + f_2(v) + f_3(w) = f_4(q)$ may be repreresented by a combination of Cartesian co-ordinate charts.   For example, consider the relation $u + v + w = q$.   Let

$$u + v = T \tag{1}$$

and $$T + w = q \tag{2}$$

Each of these equations is of the form $f_1(u) + f_2(v) = f_3(w)$ and can be represented by a family of parallel lines.   The first equation, $u + v = T$, is shown in Figure 6, and the second equation, $T + w = q$, is of similar form and is represented by Figure 7.

Obviously, not much is gained by solving the given equation, $u + v + w = q$, by parts as shown in Figures 6 and 7.   A more effective arrangement would make it possible to use values of u, v, and w directly without first determining the value of T.   This is quite possible.   First, let us analyze what happened in Figures 6 and 7.   The equation $u + v = T$, written in the slope intercept form, would be $v = -u + T$, showing that for any value of T, we have a line with a negative slope of one and an intercept equal to T. Similarly, the equation $T + w = q$ would be $w = -T + q$, showing that for any value of q, we have a line with a negative slope of one and an intercept equal to q.

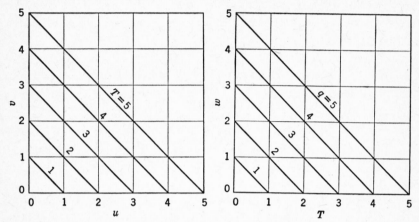

Fig. 6. Cartesian Co-ordinate Representation of the Equation, $u + v = T$.

Fig. 7. Cartesian Co-ordinate Representation of the Equation, $T + w = q$.

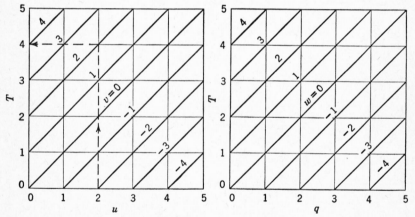

Fig. 8. Cartesian Co-ordinate Representation of the Equation, $T = u + v$. *Example*: When $u = 2$ and $v = 2$; $T = 4$.

Fig. 9. Cartesian Co-ordinate Representation for the Equation, $T = q - w$.

Now, suppose we consider equation $T = u + v$, with T replacing y and u replacing x in the usual equation, $y = mx + b$. This will result in the graphic representation shown in Figure 8. Similarly, the equation $T + w = q$ may be rewritten as $T = q - w$. The latter expression is shown graphically in Figure 9.

By combining the two charts as shown in Figure 10 it is now possible to eliminate the graduations of the T scale, and, in fact, the entire T scale, since it is common to both charts, and read u, v, w, and q directly. This method may be extended further for the solution of equations involving more than four variables.

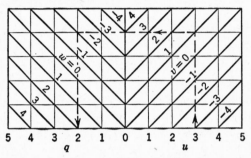

FIG. 10. Combination of Figures 8 and 9 for the Equation, $u + v + w = q$. *Example*: When $u = 3$, $v = 1$, and $w = -2$; $q = 2$. Follow the arrows shown in chart.

If the given equation is of the form $uv = w$, logarithmic scales may be employed, thus reducing the equation to $\log u + \log v = \log w$. Figure 11 shows the graphic representation of this equation.

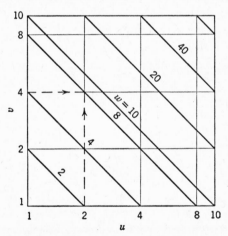

FIG. 11. Cartesian Co-ordinate Representation of the Equation, $uv = w$. *Example*: When $u = 2$ and $v = 4$; $w = 8$.

If the equation is of the form $uvw = q$, a nomogram can be designed as follows:

Let $$uv = T \qquad (1)$$

and $$Tw = q \qquad (2)$$

Equations 1 and 2 may be combined, graphically, as shown in Figure 12.

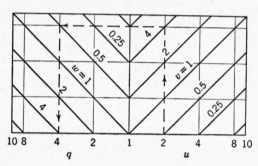

FIG. 12.   Cartesian Co-ordinate Representation of the Equation, $uvw = q$. *Example:* When $u = 2$, $v = 4$, and $w = 0.5$; $q = 4$.

Logarithmic scales may be eliminated by treating the equation $uv = w$ in the following manner. Let $y = w$ and $x = u$, from which $y = vx$. This equation represents a pencil of lines passing through the origin with slopes equal to values of v (Figure 13).

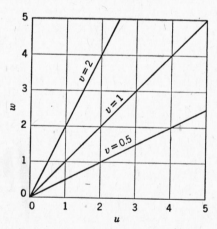

FIG. 13.   Cartesian Co-ordinate Representation of the Equation, $uv = w$.

Thus an equation of the form $uvw = q$ may be solved graphically by employing the methods set forth in the example $u + v + w = q$ (Figure 14).

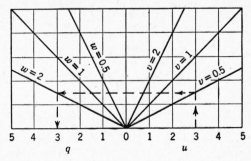

FIG. 14.　Cartesian Co-ordinate Representation of the Equation, $uvw = q$. *Example*: When $u = 3$, $v = 0.5$, and $w = 2$; $q = 3$.

An example of the use of a combination of rectangular Cartesian co-ordinate charts is shown in Figure 15—"Graph to Determine Engine Rpm."

Another example is presented in Figure 16—"Graphical Evaluation of Heat Storage and Transfer Characteristics, Q' and q'."

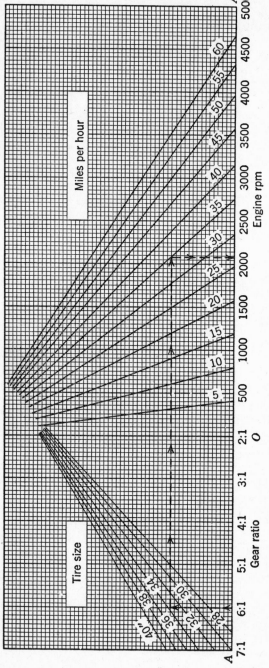

Fig. 15.   Graph to Determine Engine Rpm.   (Courtesy of Federal-Mogul Corporation, Detroit, Mich.)

Based on formula: Engine rpm (revolutions per minute) = $\dfrac{336 \times R \times S}{D}$

where R = gear ratio, S = road speed of vehicle, D = tire size, nominal outside diameter.

Example.   In a motor vehicle traveling at 35 mph, having an axle ratio of 6 to 1 and 34-in. tires, what is the engine speed in revolutions per minute?

Solution (see chart).   Locate point of 6 : 1 axle ratio on base line *A–A* and trace upwards following the arrows to the diagonal line representing the 34-in. tire size. From the intersection of these two lines, draw a line straight across (following the arrows) to the diagonal line representing 35 mph.   From this intersection, draw a straight line downwards to the base line *A–A*.   According to the calibration on base line *A–A*, the engine speed is 2075 rpm.

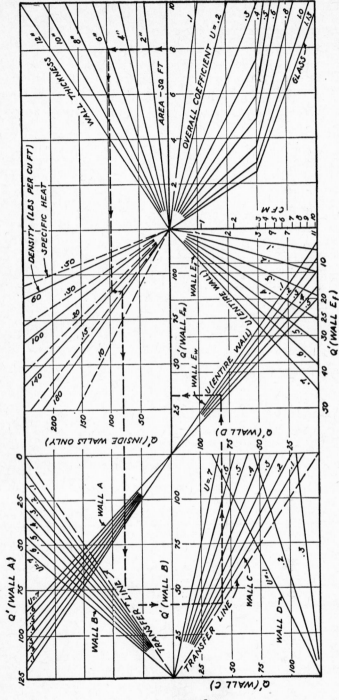

Fig. 16. Graphical Evaluation of Heat Storage and Transfer Characteristics, Q' and q'. (From B. F. Raber and F. W. Hutchinson's *Refrigeration and Air Conditioning Engineering*, John Wiley and Sons, New York, 1945. Reprinted with permission.)

Wall A. Plain; unfinished surface inside and outside. Wall B. Plain outside; $\frac{1}{2}$-in. plaster on inside. Wall C. Plain outside; $\frac{3}{4}$-in. plaster on metal lath (furred) inside. Wall D. Plain outside; $\frac{3}{4}$-in. plaster (furred) inside, with $\frac{1}{2}$-in. insulation in furred space. Wall E_w. Same wall as C but with 4-in. cut-stone veneer. Q' is for wall exclusive of veneer. Wall E_f. Same as E_w but Q' is for veneer only.

6

The simplest type of *alignment* chart consists of three parallel scales, so graduated that a straight line joining points on two of the scales will cut the third scale at a point that satisfies the relation between the variables. For example, the expression $x + y = w$ can be represented

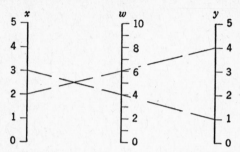

FIG. 17.   Alignment Chart for the Equation, $x + y = w$.

by the alignment chart shown in Figure 17. The line joining $x = 3$ with $y = 1$ cuts the w scale at point 4, which satisfies the equation $x + y = w$. Similarly, the line joining $x = 2$ with $y = 4$ yields the value $w = 6$.

The simplicity in using alignment charts has won much favor in technology. They, also, are especially advantageous to nontechnical personnel, who can employ them with confidence. Alignment charts are used to show the relationship between three, four, five, or more variables. Some of the charts contain diagonal and curved scales in addition to horizontal and vertical scales. In some cases, it has been found desirable to use a combination of the Cartesian co-ordinate chart and the alignment chart. An example of such a combination is shown in Figure 18—"Nomogram for Determining the Number of Seconds of Green Light for Traffic Signals." Various combinations of alignment charts can be developed. The only limitation is the ingenuity of the designer.

The introductory material that has been presented discloses the fact that nomograms may be of the concurrency (Cartesian co-ordinate) type, or of the alignment form, or of a combination of both. The major portion of the material covered in this book deals with the theory and construction of alignment charts involving straight line scales, curved scales, and combinations of straight line and curved scales. The use of determinants will be demonstrated. However, thorough treatment of the determinant method is not intended since other works which are confined to the "determinants" method only, are available.

Examples of alignment charts which may prove useful in the fields of engineering, production, business, and statistics are included in the Appendix.

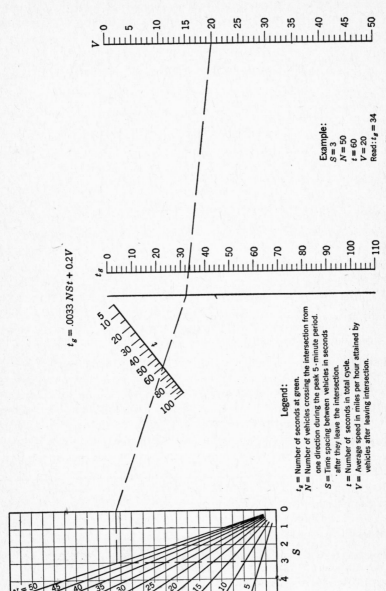

$t_g = .0033\,NSt + 0.2V$

Legend:

t_g = Number of seconds at green.
N = Number of vehicles crossing the intersection from one direction during the peak 5-minute period.
S = Time spacing between vehicles in seconds after they leave the intersection.
t = Number of seconds in total cycle.
V = Average speed in miles per hour attained by vehicles after leaving intersection.

Example:
$S = 3$
$N = 50$
$t = 60$
$V = 20$
Read: $t_g = 34$

Fig. 18.   Combination of Cartesian Co-ordinate Chart and Alignment Chart.

Chapter Two

FUNCTIONAL SCALES

The first step necessary in the design of alignment charts is a thorough understanding of the use of functional scales.

A *graphical scale* is a curved or straight line carrying graduations which correspond to a set of numbers arranged in order of magnitude. If the distances between successive points on the scale are equal for equal increments of the variable, the scale is said to be uniform; if not, the scale is non-uniform.

A *functional scale* is one on which the graduations are marked with the "values of the variable" and on which the distances to the graduations are laid off in proportion to the corresponding values of the "function of the variable." The distances are laid off from an initial point of the scale, not necessarily the zero point.

EXAMPLE

Suppose the function of u, $f(u)$, is u^3 (Figure 19). Let u vary from 0 to 5. Form the following table:

u	0	1	2	3	4	5
$f(u) = u^3$	0	1	8	27	64	125
$x = u^3$	0	1	8	27	64	125

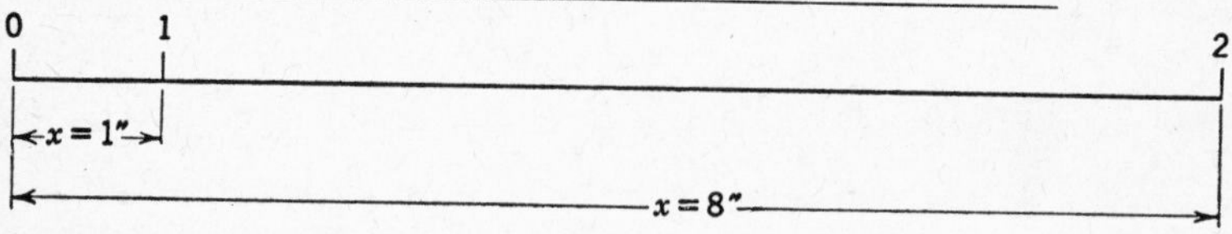

Fig. 19.

We can readily understand that the above scale would be 125 in. long if the inch is used as the unit of measure. Obviously this is not a convenient length. In order to have a scale of a more practical length, a *scale modulus* or scale multiplier is introduced, that is, $x = mu^3$ or $m = x/u^3$, where m is the scale modulus. The expression $x = mf(u)$ is called the *scale equation*.

Now suppose that the scale is to be approximately 6 in. long (Figure 20). Then $m = x/u^3 = 6/125 = 0.048$. To simplify the computational work, $m = 0.05$ will be used. This means that the scale length will be 6.25 in. instead of 6 in. The new table then is:

u	0	1	2	3	4	5
$f(u) = u^3$	0	1	8	27	64	125
$x = 0.05u^3$	0	0.05	0.40	1.35	3.20	6.25

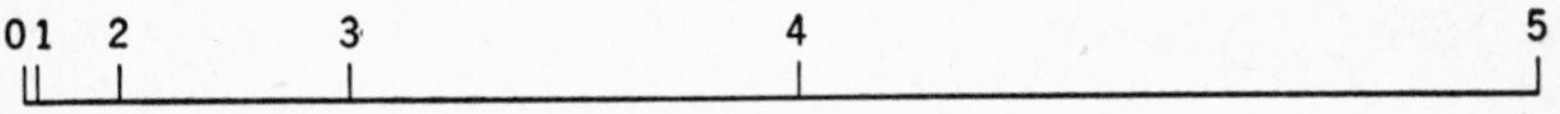

Fig. 20.   Functional Scale for $f(u) = u^3$.

In the practical use of functional scales further subdivision of the scale into fifths or tenths may be advisable. Suppose that the range of the variable is from 2 to 4 and that the scale length is approximately 6 in. (Figure 21). In this case $x = m[f(u_2) - f(u_1)] = m(4^3 - 2^3) = 56m$ or $m = 6/56 = 0.107$. For convenience we shall use 0.1. Then we have the table:

u	2	3	4
$f(u) = u^3$	8	27	64
$x = 0.1(u^3 - 2^3)$	0	1.9	5.6

Fig. 21.   Functional Scale for $f(u) = u^3$.

It should be noted that in this case the initial point of the scale is 2, not 0.

The distance between any two graduations, u_1 and u_2, is equal to $x = m[f(u_2) - f(u_1)]$.

Any unit of length other than inches could be adopted as the unit of measure. It is most important to observe (1) that the distance between any two points on the scale is equal to the product of the modulus and the difference in the *values of the function* for the two points, *not* the *values of the variables;* and (2) that the points are marked with the value of the variable.

Suppose that the $f(u)$ is $2u^3$. The scale equation is $x = m(2u^3)$. If u varies from 0 to 4, and the scale length is to be approximately 6 in., then

$$m = \frac{6}{2(4^3)} = \frac{6}{128} = 0.047$$

For convenience, $m = 0.05$ will be used. This lengthens the scale to 6.4 in.

Hence, $x = 0.05(2u^3)$ or $x = 0.1u^3$. It is important to note that 0.1 is the *effective modulus*, whereas 0.05 is the actual modulus of the scale. The effective modulus is used in graduating the scale. The "actual modulus" is necessary in the location of scales that occur in alignment chart design. This distinction will be evident later when the design and construction of alignment charts are considered.

If the function of u is $(u + 2)$ (Figure 22), then the scale equation is $x = m(u + 2)$. If u varies from 0 to 12, and the scale is 6 in. long, then

$$m = \frac{6 \text{ in.}}{[(12 + 2) - (0 + 2)]} = \frac{6}{12} = \frac{1}{2} \text{ in.}$$

or $\qquad x = \frac{1}{2}(u + 2)$

u	0	1	2	..	12
$f(u) = (u + 2)$	2	3	4	..	14
$x = \frac{1}{2}(u + 2)$	1	1.5	2	..	7

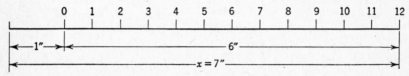

FIG. 22. Scale for the Function, $(u + 2)$.

In this case, the constant 2 merely shifts the zero point of the scale a distance from the reference point of the scale equal to $\frac{1}{2}(0 + 2) = 1$ in. Except for the shift of the zero point, the scale is the same as though the $f(u)$ were u, because the total length of the scale is $x = \frac{1}{2} \times 12 = 6$ in., which is the same as $x = \frac{1}{2}[(12 + 2) - (0 + 2)] = 6$ in.

EXAMPLE 1

$$f(u) = \sqrt{u}$$

where u varies from 0 to 100, scale length approximately 6 in. (Figure 23).

$$m_u = \frac{6}{\sqrt{100} - \sqrt{0}} = \frac{6}{10}$$

$$x_u = 0.6\sqrt{u}$$

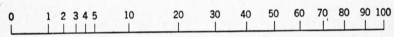

FIG. 23. Functional Scale for $f(u) = \sqrt{u}$.

EXAMPLE 2

$$f(u) = \frac{1}{u^2}$$

where u varies from 1 to 3, scale length 6 in. (Figure 24).

$$m_u = \frac{6}{\left[\dfrac{1}{1^2} - \dfrac{1}{3^2}\right]} = 6.75; \quad x_u = 6.75\left[\frac{1}{u^2} - \frac{1}{1^2}\right]$$

u	1	2	3
$f(u) = \dfrac{1}{u^2}$	1	$\frac{1}{4}$	$\frac{1}{9}$
$x_u = 6.75\left[\dfrac{1}{u^2} - \dfrac{1}{1^2}\right]$	0	$-\frac{81}{16}$	-6

Note that the negative distances, x_u, are laid off to the left of point 1, since distances laid off to the right have been regarded as positive.

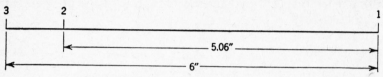

FIG. 24. Functional Scale for $f(u) = 1/u^2$.

EXAMPLE 3

$$f(u) = \log u$$

where u varies from 2 to 10, scale length, 7 in. (Figure 25).

$$m_u = \frac{7}{\log 10 - \log 2} = \frac{7}{\log 5} = 10$$

$$x_u = 10(\log u - \log 2)$$

A few points are tabulated below:

u	2	4	8	10
$\log u$	0.301	0.602	0.903	1.000
$x_u = 10(\log u - \log 2)$	0	3.01	6.02	6.99

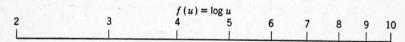

FIG. 25. Functional Scale for $f(u) = \log u$.

Suggestions for Drawing Scales:

(1) Make the shortest strokes $\frac{1}{10}$ in.
(2) Make the intermediate strokes $\frac{3}{20}$ in.
(3) Make the longest strokes $\frac{3}{16}$ in.
(4) Adjacent strokes should be not less than $\frac{1}{20}$ in. apart, or more than $\frac{1}{2}$ in.

(5) The distance between labeled strokes should be not less than $\frac{1}{4}$ in.

(6) The interval between units should be divided into fifths or tenths, if necessary.

Suggestions for Graphic Precision:

(1) Layout lines should be sharp and light.

(2) Finish lines should be sharp and dark.

(3) Use as large a scale as possible.

(4) If the chart is to be reduced, use a reducing glass to determine the relative weights of lines required in the original drawing.

EXERCISES

Functional Scales

1. Construct a scale for the function $f(u) = \sqrt[3]{u}$. u varies from 0 to 8. Scale length about 6 in.

2. Construct a scale for the function $f(u) = 2 \log u$. u varies from 10 to 300. Scale length about 6 in.

3. Construct a scale for the function $f(u) = \cos u$. u varies from 0° to 90°. Scale length 6 in.

4. Change the range of the variable of problem 3 to 0° to 180° and construct a scale of the same modulus.

5. Construct scales for the functions $f(u) = \log 1/u$, $\log u$, $\log u^2$, $\log u^3$. u varies from 1 to 10. Scale length about 6 in. Write the scale equations for each case.

6. Construct a scale for the function $f(u) = 1/u$. u varies from $\frac{1}{2}$ to ∞. Scale length about 7 in. Where would be the point, $u = 0$?

7. Construct a scale for the function $f(u) = u^{3/2}$. Range of the variable 0 to 10. Scale length about 6 in.

8. On one side of a line construct a scale for u^2, on the other side $u^2 + 3$. Use the same reference point and same modulus. Range 1 to 5. Do the same for $\log u$ and $\log (u + 2)$. Scale lengths about 6 in.

9. Explain the effect of the constant K on the scales in the following scale equations:

$$x_u = mKu \tag{1}$$

$$x_u = m(u + K) \tag{2}$$

$$x_u = m \log u^K \tag{3}$$

$$x_u = m \log (u + K) \tag{4}$$

10. Construct a scale for the function $f(t)$ given by the following table, where $f(t)$ is the vapor pressure in air corresponding to t, the air temperature, in degrees Fahrenheit:

t	$f(t)$	t	$f(t)$
0	0.0383	55	0.432
5	0.0491	60	0.517
10	0.0631	65	0.616
15	0.0810	70	0.732
20	0.1026	75	0.866
25	0.130	80	1.022
30	0.164	85	1.201
35	0.203	90	1.408
40	0.247	95	1.645
45	0.298	100	1.916
50	0.360		

11. Given the following experimental data:

u	$f(u)$	u	$f(u)$
0	0.05	26	0.12
11	0.065	32	0.17
18	0.085	40	0.33

Draw a smooth curve through the points and construct a functional scale for $f(u)$ from the curve.

12. Construct a scale for the wave length of the various colors of light:

Color	Wave Length	
Violet	4000 Angstrom units *	
Blue	4500	" "
Green	5200	" "
Yellow	5700	" "
Red	6500	" "

---

* The Angstrom unit = one ten-millionth of a millimeter, i.e., 0.0000001 mm.

ADJACENT SCALES FOR THE SOLUTION OF EQUATIONS OF THE FORM

$$f_1(u) = f_2(v)$$

Equations of the above form may be solved by graduating both sides of one line in such a manner that a point on the scale will give values which satisfy the given equation. The scale equations are:

$$X_u = m_u f_1(u) \quad \text{and} \quad X_v = m_v f_2(v)$$

Since $f_1(u) = f_2(v)$ and $X_u = X_v$, i.e., for any point on the scale; then, $m_u = m_v$.

EXAMPLE 1

Consider the relation, $2.54I = C$ (Figure 26), where I represents inches and C represents centimeters. Let I vary from 0 to 10; scale length, 6 in. If we rewrite the given equation so that

$$I = \frac{C}{2.54}$$

Then, $\qquad X_I = m_I I, \quad \text{or} \quad 6 = m_I 10$

from which $\qquad m_I = 0.6$

Thus, the scale equation is $X_I = 0.6I$. The scale equation for C is $X_c = 0.6(C/2.54) = 0.236C$.

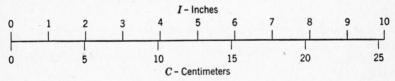

FIG. 26. Adjacent Scales for the Equation, $2.54I = C$.

Note: Having computed the scale modulus for I, the *same* modulus must be used for C. If the scale modulus for C had been computed first, then this modulus would apply to I.

EXAMPLE 2

$C = \pi D$ (Figure 27). C = circumference of a circle, with diameter D. Let D vary from 2 to 10 in. Scale length, 6 in.

The scale equations are:

$$X_c = m_c \left[\frac{C}{\pi} \right]$$

and $X_D = m_D D;$ or $6 = m_D[10 - 2];$ $m_D = \frac{3}{4}$

hence $X_D = \frac{3}{4}[D - 2]$

and $X_c = \frac{3}{4}\frac{C}{\pi} = \frac{3C}{4\pi} = 0.239C$

To locate a point on the scale C. For example, $C = 10$.

Point 10 on the C scale is 2.39 in. from the zero point of that scale ($X_c = 0.239[10]$). Since point 2 of the D scale is $1\frac{1}{2}$ in., ($X = \frac{3}{4} \times 2$) from the zero point of the D scale, point 10 is $(2.39 - 1.50) = 0.89$ in.

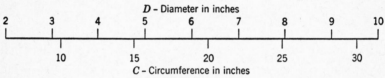

FIG. 27. Adjacent Scales for the Equation, $C = \pi D$.

to right of point 2.   (It should be observed that $C = 0$ when $D = 0$.) Point 20 of the C scale is 2.39 in. to the right of point 10 ($X_c = 0.239 \times [20 - 10]) = 2.39$ in.). Points between 10 and 20 can easily be located by subdivision. Points beyond 20 can be located in a similar manner. Of course, a point of the C scale could be located by solving C from a specific value of D. The scale could then be graduated from the scale equation,

$$X_c = 0.239[C_2 - C_1]$$

EXAMPLE 3

$U = \sin V$ (Figure 28). Let V vary from $0°$ to $90°$; scale length, 6 in.

The scale equations are:

$$X_u = m_u U \tag{1}$$

and

$$X_v = m_v \sin V \tag{2}$$

From equation (2) $6 = m_v(\sin 90° - \sin 0°)$; $m_v = 6$. Hence the scale equations are:

$$X_u = 6U$$

and

$$X_v = 6 \sin V$$

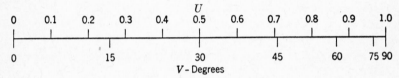

FIG. 28. Adjacent Scales for the Equation, $U = \sin V$.

EXAMPLE 4

$V = \frac{4}{3}\pi r^3$ (Figure 29). $V =$ the volume of a sphere of radius r. Let r vary from 0 to 5 in.; length of scale to be approximately 6 in. Then

$$X_r = m_r r^3; \quad \text{and} \quad X_v = m_v \frac{3V}{4\pi}$$

$$m_r = \tfrac{6}{125} = 0.048.$$

For convenience, use $m_r = 0.05$. Then

$$X_r = 0.05r^3 \quad \text{and} \quad X_v = 0.05 \times \frac{3V}{4\pi} = 0.0119V$$

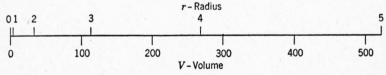

FIG. 29. Adjacent Scales for the Equation, $V = \frac{4}{3}\pi r^3$.

NON-ADJACENT SCALES FOR THE SOLUTION OF
EQUATIONS OF THE FORM

$$f_1(u) = f_2(v)$$

In the foregoing material it was pointed out that the *same* modulus was used in each scale equation. It may be desirable to use two dif-

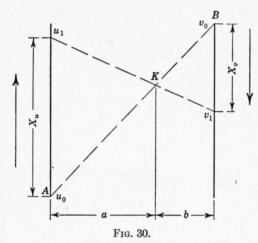

Fig. 30.

ferent moduli. This can be done by separating the scales in the following manner. (See Figure 30.)

Let $$X_u = m_u f_1(u) \tag{1}$$

and $$X_v = m_v f_2(v) \tag{2}$$

u_0 and v_0 are zero values of the functions of u and v; and K is a point located on line AB so that any line passing through K and a selected point on the u or v scale will cut the other scale in a value which satisfies the equation.

From the similar triangles Au_1K and Bv_1K,

$$\frac{X_u}{X_v} = \frac{AK}{KB} = \frac{a}{b}$$

Therefore $\dfrac{m_u f_1(u)}{m_v f_2(v)} = \dfrac{a}{b}$ (from equations 1 and 2 above)

Since $f_1(u) = f_2(v)$,

$$\frac{a}{b} = \frac{m_u}{m_v}$$

Hence point K can be located on the diagonal AB by dividing it into the ratio

$$\frac{AK}{KB} = \frac{a}{b} = \frac{m_u}{m_v}$$

EXAMPLE

Again consider the equation, $2.54I = C$ (Figure 31).

Let $$X_I = \tfrac{1}{2}I; \quad X_c = \left(\frac{2.54}{4}\right)\left[\frac{C}{2.54}\right] = \frac{C}{4}$$

$$\frac{m_I}{m_C} = \frac{\frac{1}{2}}{\frac{2.54}{4}} = \frac{1}{1.27}$$

EXERCISES

Adjacent Scales or Non-Adjacent Scales

13. Construct (*a*) adjacent and (*b*) non-adjacent scales for converting Fahrenheit readings to centigrade.

$$C = \tfrac{5}{9}(F - 32) \qquad C(-40° \text{ to } 100°)$$

14. Construct adjacent scales for the equation area of circle, $A = \pi d^2/4$. $d(0 \text{ to } 20 \text{ in.})$. (Do not use log scales.)

15. Use logarithmic scales in problem 14. What are the advantages of each method? Disadvantages?

16. Construct adjacent scales for the equation $t = 2\pi\sqrt{L/g}$, the period of a simple pendulum of length, L, and with $g = 32.2$. L (1 to 5 ft).

17. Construct adjacent scales for the equation, $X = \log_e y$. $y(1 \text{ to } 10)$.

18. On a log scale using the base 10, the distance between 1 and 2, 2 and 4, 4 and 8 are equal. Is this true when "e" is used as the base?

19. Construct adjacent scales for the vapor pressure in air as a function of temperature as given in problem 10.

20. Construct non-adjacent scales for the compound interest law, $P = A(1 + R)^n$, where P is the principal, R the rate of interest, A the amount, and n the number of times compounded. Let $A = \$1.00$, $R = 5\%$. Then $P = (1.05)^n$. n varies from (0 to 20). How can this chart be used if $n = 30$?

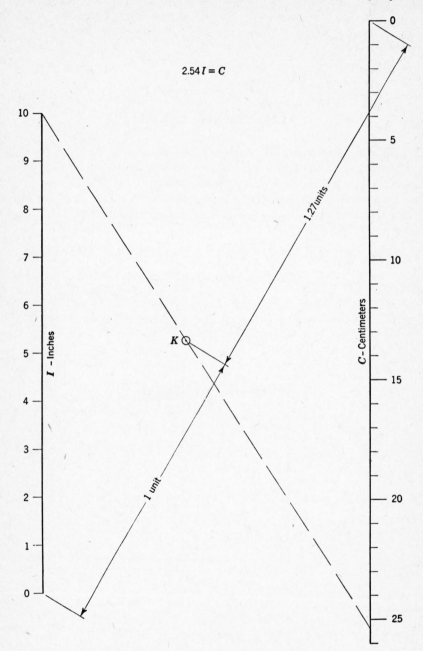

Fig. 31.   Separated Scales for the Relation, $2.54I = C$.

Eckel

Chapter Three

ALIGNMENT CHARTS

An alignment chart in its simplest form consists of three parallel scales so graduated that a straight line cutting the scales will determine three points whose values satisfy the given equation.

In general, alignment charts may consist of three or more straight-line scales, of curved scales, or of combinations of both.

ALIGNMENT CHARTS FOR EQUATIONS OF THE FORM

$$f_1(u) + f_2(v) = f_3(w)$$

Suppose we have three parallel scales (Figure 32), A, B, and C, so graduated that lines (isopleths) 1 and 2 cut the scales in values which satisfy the equation $f_1(u) + f_2(v) = f_3(w)$. Now,

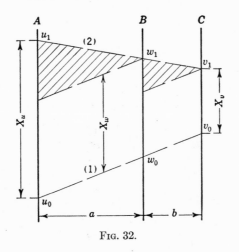

Fig. 32.

$$X_u = m_u[f_1(u_1) - f_1(u_0)]$$

$$X_v = m_v[f_2(v_1) - f_2(v_0)]$$

$$X_w = m_w[f_3(w_1) - f_3(w_0)]$$

25

If u_0, v_0, w_0, represent zero values of the functions, and if line 2 is any line, we may drop the subscripts and write simply

$$X_u = m_u f_1(u) \tag{1}$$

$$X_v = m_v f_2(v) \tag{2}$$

$$X_w = m_w f_3(w) \tag{3}$$

Let us agree further that the spacing of the scales is in the ratio a/b. If we graduate the scales for $f_1(u)$ and $f_2(v)$ in accordance with their scale equations (1) and (2), respectively, what will be the modulus for the scale equation of $f_3(w)$ and what will the ratio a/b equal if the chart satisfies this relation $f_1(u) + f_2(v) = f_3(w)$?

In Figure 32 draw lines through points w_1 and v_1 parallel to line u_0v_0. The shaded triangles are similar by construction, hence,

$$\frac{X_u - X_w}{X_w - X_v} = \frac{a}{b}$$

$$X_u b + X_v a = X_w (a + b)$$

$$\frac{X_u b}{ab} + \frac{X_v a}{ab} = X_w \left(\frac{a + b}{ab} \right)$$

or

$$\frac{X_u}{a} + \frac{X_v}{b} = \frac{X_w}{\dfrac{ab}{a + b}}$$

Since

$$X_u = m_u f_1(u)$$

$$X_v = m_v f_2(v)$$

$$X_w = m_w f_3(w)$$

$$\frac{m_u f_1(u)}{a} + \frac{m_v f_2(v)}{b} = \frac{m_w f_3(w)}{\dfrac{ab}{a + b}}$$

If $f_1(u) + f_2(v) = f_3(w)$, then

$$m_u = a; \quad m_v = b$$

Therefore

$$\frac{a}{b} = \frac{m_u}{m_v}$$

and

$$m_w = \frac{ab}{a + b} = \frac{m_u m_v}{m_u + m_v}$$

Thus, to construct an alignment chart for an equation of the form, $f_1(u) + f_2(v) = f_3(w)$,

(a) Place the parallel scales for u and v a convenient distance apart.

(b) Graduate them in accordance with their scale equations, $X_u = m_u f_1(u)$ and $X_v = m_v f_2(v)$.

(c) Locate the scale for w so that its distance from the u scale is to its distance from the v scale as $m_u/m_v = a/b$.

(d) Graduate the w scale from its scale equation, $X_w = \dfrac{m_u m_v}{m_u + m_v} f_3(w)$.

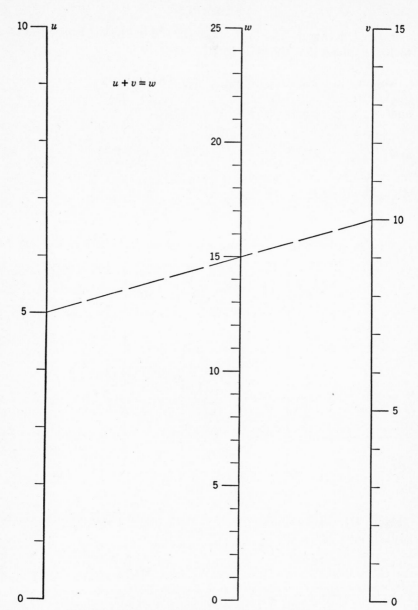

Fig. 33.   Alignment Chart for the Equation, $u + v = w$.

EXAMPLE

$u + v = w$ (Figure 33). Let u vary from 0 to 10; and v vary from 0 to 15. Suppose that the scale lengths are to be 6 in.

Now $\qquad m_u = \frac{6}{10} = 0.6; \quad X_u = 0.6u$

and $\qquad m_v = \frac{6}{15} = 0.4; \quad X_v = 0.4v$

and $\qquad m_w = \dfrac{0.6 \times 0.4}{0.6 + 0.4} = 0.24; \quad X_w = 0.24w$

$$\frac{m_u}{m_v} = \frac{0.6}{0.4} = \frac{3}{2} = \frac{a}{b}$$

Now suppose that it is desirable to cut off the chart at the line 1

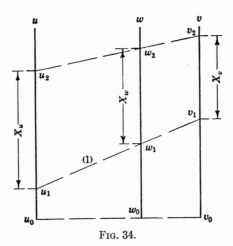

Fig. 34.

(Figure 34), eliminating the portion below line 1. The scale equations will then be (using line 1 as the base line):

$$X_u = m_u[f_1(u_2) - f_1(u_1)]$$

$$X_v = m_v[f_2(v_2) - f_2(v_1)]$$

$$X_w = m_w[f_3(w_2) - f_3(w_1)]$$

where u_1, v_1, and w_1 satisfy the equation $f_1(u) + f_2(v) = f_3(w)$.

EXAMPLE 1

$u + v = w$ (Figure 35). Let u vary from 2 to 6; and v vary from 3 to 8. Length of scales, 6 in.

Now
$$m_u{}^* = \frac{6}{6-2} = \frac{3}{2}; \quad X_u = \frac{3}{2}(u-2)$$

$$m_v = \frac{6}{8-3} = \frac{6}{5}; \quad X_v = \frac{6}{5}(v-3)$$

Since
$$m_w = \frac{m_u m_v}{m_u + m_v}$$

$$m_w = \frac{\frac{3}{2} \times \frac{6}{5}}{\frac{3}{2} + \frac{6}{5}} = \frac{\frac{18}{10}}{\frac{27}{10}} = \frac{2}{3}$$

Since $u_1 = 2$ and $v_1 = 3$, therefore $w_1 = 5$. (From the original equation $u + v = w$.) Hence,

$$X_w = \tfrac{2}{3}[w - 5]$$

$$\frac{a}{b} = \frac{m_u}{m_v} = \frac{\frac{3}{2}}{\frac{6}{5}} = \frac{5}{4}$$

Form the following tables:

u	2	3	4	5	6
$f_1(u) = u$	2	3	4	5	6
$X_u = \frac{3}{2}[u - 2]$	0	1.5 in.	3.0 in.	4.5 in.	6.0 in.

* Remember $X_u = m_u f(u)$. Therefore, $m_u = \dfrac{X_u}{f_1(u_2) - f_1(u_1)}$. In this case $X_u = 6$ in. and $[f_1(u_2) - f_1(u_1)] = (6 - 2)$.

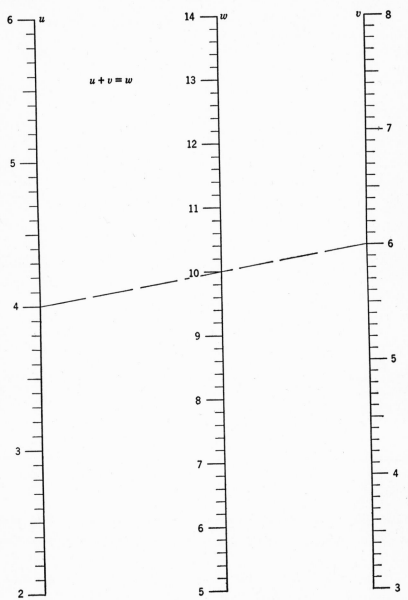

FIG. 35.   Alignment Chart for the Equation, $u + v = w$.

v	3	4	5	6	7	8
$f_2(v) = v$	3	4	5	6	7	8
$X_v = \frac{6}{5}[v - 3]$	0	1.2 in.	2.4 in.	3.6 in.	4.8 in.	6.0 in.

w	5	6	7	...	14
$f_3(w) = w$	5	6	7	...	14
$X_w = \frac{2}{3}[w - 5]$	0	$\frac{2}{3}$ in.	$\frac{4}{3}$ in.	...	6 in.

Much of the calculations set forth in the above tables can be eliminated if we compute the location of the end points for each scale, and
then project the other points geometrically.

EXAMPLE 2

$I = \frac{1}{12}bd^3$ (Figure 36), where I is the moment of inertia of a rectangle about its axis parallel to b, where b is the width, and d is the
height of the rectangle.

Let b vary from 1 to 10 in., d from 1 to 10 in. Length of scales, 6 in.
The equation, which may be written $bd^3 = 12I$, is put in the type form
by taking logarithms; thus we obtain

$$\log b + 3 \log d = \log I + \log 12$$

Now the moduli m_b and m_d are computed as follows:

$$m_b = \frac{6}{\log 10 - \log 1} = 6; \qquad X_b = 6 \log b$$

$$m_d = \frac{6}{3 \log 10 - 3 \log 1} = 2; \quad X_d = 2(3 \log d) = 6 \log d$$

It should be pointed out that the function of d is $3 \log d$, the modulus
2 is the "actual modulus" which is used in locating the I scale, and the
coefficient 6 is the *effective modulus* which is used in graduating the d
scale.

$$m_I = \frac{6 \times 2}{6 + 2} = \frac{12}{8} = \frac{3}{2}; \quad X_I = \frac{3}{2}(\log I + \log 12)$$

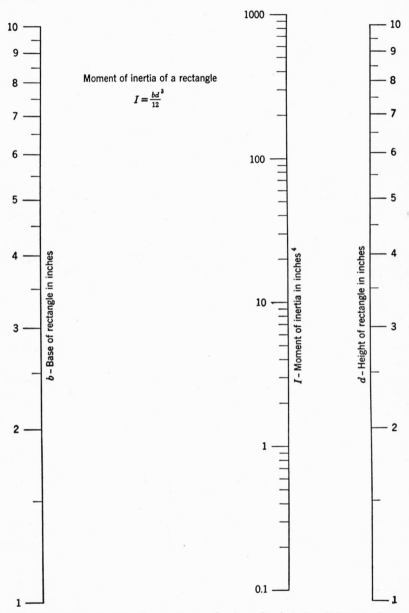

Moment of inertia of a rectangle

$$I = \frac{bd^3}{12}$$

b – Base of rectangle in inches

I – Moment of inertia in inches^4

d – Height of rectangle in inches

FIG. 36.   Moment of Inertia of a Rectangle about Its Axis Parallel to the Base.

Note carefully that the actual moduli of b and d are used in computing m_I. Form the following table:

b	1	2	3	$\ldots$	10
$f(b) = \log b$	0	0.301	0.477	$\ldots$	1.000
$X_b = 6 \log b$	0	0.81	2.86	$\ldots$	6.00

The table for d will be the same as the above since $m_d = 6$ (effective modulus).

Now we can graduate the scales for b and d in accordance with the scale equations $X_b = 6 \log b$ and $X_d = 2(3 \log d)$. The scales are placed a convenient distance apart. The position of the I scale is determined from the ratio $m_b/m_d = \frac{6}{2} = \frac{3}{1}$. Our next step is to locate one point on the I scale, i.e., point 1. Suppose we let $d = 2$. Then $b = 12I/d^3$ or $b = (12 \times 1)/8 = 1.5$. The line joining $b = 1.5$ and $d = 2$ cuts the I scale at point 1. Now we can locate other points on the I scale from the scale equation

$$X_I = \frac{6 \times 2}{6 + 2} [\log I - \log 1]$$

or $$X_I = 1.5(\log I)$$

This means that points on the I scale are laid off from point 1. If the selected point on the I scale were 10, then graduations would be laid off from this point in accordance with the scale equation:

$$X_I = 1.5[\log I - \log 10]$$

or $$X_I = 1.5(\log I - 1)$$

If the equation were $f_1(u) - f_2(v) = f_3(w)$, the scale equations would be:

$$X_u = m_u f_1(u) \tag{1}$$

$$X_v = m_v[-f_2(v)] \tag{2}$$

$$X_w = \frac{m_u m_v}{m_u + m_v} f_3(w) \tag{3}$$

The negative sign in equation 2 implies that positive values of $f_2(v)$ are laid off downwardly if we agree to lay off positive values of $f_1(u)$ upwardly.

EXAMPLE

$u - v = w$ (Figure 37). Suppose u varies from 0 to 5, and v varies from 2 to 6. Scale lengths, 6 units (inches, centimeters, or any convenient length).

$$m_u = \tfrac{6}{5}; \quad X_u = \tfrac{6}{5}u$$

$$m_v = \tfrac{6}{4} = \tfrac{3}{2}; \quad X_v = \tfrac{3}{2}(-v) = -\tfrac{3}{2}v$$

$$m_w = \frac{\tfrac{6}{5} \times \tfrac{3}{2}}{\tfrac{6}{5} + \tfrac{3}{2}} = \frac{\tfrac{9}{5}}{\tfrac{27}{10}} = \frac{2}{3}; \quad X_w = \frac{2}{3}w$$

$$\frac{m_u}{m_v} = \frac{\tfrac{6}{5}}{\tfrac{3}{2}} = \frac{4}{5}$$

Scales u and v are placed a convenient distance apart. Scale u is graduated in accordance with the scale equation $X_u = \tfrac{6}{5}u$. Scale v is

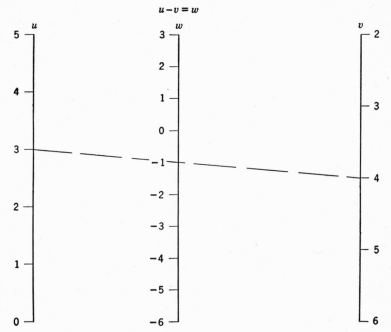

FIG. 37. Alignment Chart for the Equation, $u - v = w$.

graduated from the equation $X_v = \tfrac{3}{2}v$. This is done by locating point 2 on the upper end of the v scale, and laying off distances equal to $\tfrac{3}{2}$ units for each point 3, 4, 5, and 6.

NOTE: POSITIVE VALUES OF "V" ARE LAID OFF DOWN-WARDLY!

A point on the w scale can be located by solving the original equation, $u - v = w$.

Example: Let $u = 3$ and $v = 4$; then $w = -1$ (of course, in this case it might have been simpler to locate the zero point on the w scale by letting u and v equal the same value). Having located one point on w, other points can be located from the scale equation $X_w = \frac{2}{3}w$; that is, the distance between consecutive points is $\frac{2}{3}$ units.

EXERCISES

Hydraulics

21(a). $Q = 3.33bH^{3/2}$ (Francis weir formula for a rectangular weir)

where Q = discharge (cubic feet per second), b = width of weir (3 to 20 ft), H = head above crest (0.5 to 1.5 ft).

21(b). Use a double graduation of the Q scale of part a to indicate gallons per minute.

22. $V = C\sqrt{2gH}$ (velocity of water, in feet per second, through an orifice due to a head of water, H)

where $g = 32.2$, C = a coefficient for the orifice depending on shape, etc. (0.6 to 1), and H = head of water (1 to 15 ft).

23. The horsepower of a jet of water is given by the equation

$$HP = \frac{Wv^2}{2g \times 550}$$

where W = the weight of water per second (1 to 100 lb) and v = the velocity of water in feet per second (1 to 50).

If desired, since one cubic foot of water is 62.4 lb, the formula may be converted to

$$HP = \frac{Qv^2 \times 62.4}{2g \times 550}$$

where Q = the quantity in cubic feet per second and $g = 32.2$.

24. $H = \dfrac{P}{W}$ (head in feet of a liquid equivalent to the pressure, P, in pounds per square foot)

where W is weight per cubic foot of the liquid. If P is in pounds per square inch, $H = 144P/W$.

Let P vary from 5 to 300 psi. For W use the common fluids such as water and kerosene.

25. $H = 0.38 \dfrac{V^{1.86}}{D^{1.25}}$ (friction head for water flowing in 1000 ft of pipe)

where V = velocity of flow in feet per second (2 to 15) and D = diameter of pipe in feet (1 to 6).

Strength of Materials

26. $\qquad R_s = \dfrac{\pi}{4} d^2 f_s$ (allowable strength of a rivet)

where d = diameter of rivet ($\frac{1}{8}$ to 1 in.) and f_s = allowable unit shearing stress of material (3000 to 15,000 psi).

27. $\qquad \rho^2 = \dfrac{I}{A}$ (radius of gyration of a section)

where I = moment of inertia (1 to 1000 in.⁴) and A = area of section (1 to 100 sq in.).

28. $\qquad f = \dfrac{C\pi E}{\left(\dfrac{L}{P}\right)^2}$ (critical stress in a long column)

Let $C = 1$, fixity coefficient for pin ended column, E = modulus of elasticity (10×10^6 to 30×10^6 psi), and (L/P) = slenderness ratio (70 to 200).

29. $\qquad e = \dfrac{f x}{E} - \dfrac{m f y}{E}$ (unit elongation in the x direction)

where f_x = unit stress in x direction (0 to 50,000 psi), f_y = unit stress in y direction (0 to 50,000 psi), $m = 0.3$, and $E = 30 \times 10^6$ psi for structural steel.

Mechanical

30. $\quad \text{BHP} = \dfrac{d^2 n}{2.5}$ (Association of Automobile Manufacturers formula)

where d = diameter of cylinders ($1\frac{3}{4}$ in. to 5%), n = number of cylinders (2, 4, 6, 8, 12), and BHP = brake horsepower.

31. $\quad d = 2.87 \sqrt[3]{\dfrac{\text{HP}}{\text{RPM}}}$ (diameter in inches of a spur gear steel shaft)

where HP = horsepower (100 to 2000) and RPM = revolutions per minute (100 to 1000).

32. $\quad P_m = \dfrac{(1 + \log_e R)}{R} P_1$ (absolute mean pressure of expanded steam)

where P_1 = absolute initial pressure (50 to 350 psi) and R = ratio of expansion = V/V_1 (1 to 10).

33. $P = CF^{3/4}D^{14/15}$ (pressure in pounds on tool when cutting cast iron)

where F = feed (0.01 to 0.20 in.), D = depth of cut ($\frac{1}{8}$ to 1 in.), C = 45,000 for soft cast iron, and C = 69,000 for hard cast iron.

34. $F = \dfrac{P^{0.97}A_0}{60}$ (flow of steam through a steam nozzle in pounds per second)

where P = absolute initial pressure (5 to 300 psi) and A_0 = area at throat (1 to 30 sq in.).

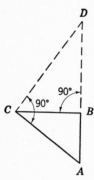

35. $S = \dfrac{\pi DN}{12}$

where S is the cutting speed in feet per minute in lath or boring mill, D = diameter of work (0.25 to 12.5 in.), and N = (10 to 1000 rpm).

Civil

36. $C = 0.0000065L(T - T_0)$ (change in length of a steel tape due to a difference in temp. $[T - T_0]$ from the standard temperature, T_0)

where L is the measured length (10 to 100 ft), and ($T - T_0$) varies from (5° to 75°).

37. In the figure shown it is required to find the inaccessible distance BD, which is equal to $BD = BC^2/AB$. BC varies (1 to 10) and AB varies (1 to 10).

38. For the simple curve $T = R \tan \Delta/2$, where R is usually obtained from the degree of curvature and is equal to

$$R = \frac{5729.65}{(\text{degree of curv.})} = \frac{5729.65}{D}$$

where D, degree of curvature, varies (1° to 30°) and Δ varies (10° to 150°).

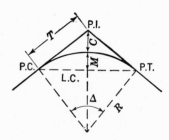

39. L.C. $= 2R \sin \dfrac{\Delta}{2}$ (long chord as shown in figure of problem 38)

Use limits of problem 38.

40. $$C = R \text{ exsec } \frac{\Delta}{2} \text{ (external distance of a curve)}$$

See figure of problem 38. Use same limits.

41. $$M = R \text{ vers } \frac{\Delta}{2} \text{ (midordinate of a curve)}$$

See figure of problem 38. Use same limits.

42. $$L = \frac{\Delta}{D} 100 \text{ (length of the curve)}$$

See figure of problem 38. Use same limits.

43. $$R = \frac{50}{\sin \frac{D}{2}} \text{ (radius of curvature for 100-ft chords)}$$

See figure of problem 38. Use same limits.

44. $$R = \frac{\frac{C}{2}}{\sin \frac{CD}{200}}$$

where it is recommended that

$$C = 100 \text{ ft for } 0° < D < 7°$$

$$C = 50 \text{ ft for } 7° < D < 14°$$

$$C = 25 \text{ ft for } 14° < D < 28°$$

$$C = 10 \text{ ft for } D > 28°$$

45. In a railroad curve as shown the offset x of B from the tangent at A is

$$X = \frac{C^2}{2R}$$

where C varies (10 to 100 ft) and R varies (100 to 6000 ft)

Electrical

46. $P = \dfrac{E^2}{R}$ (power in watts used in passing an electric current through a resistance, R)

where E = voltage (10 to 220 volts) and R = resistance (10 to 1000 ohms).

47. $\dfrac{1}{R} = \dfrac{1}{R_1} + \dfrac{1}{R_2}$ (sum of resistances in parallel)

where R_1 (1 to 100 ohms) and R_2 (1 to 100 ohms).

48. $X = \dfrac{1{,}000{,}000}{2\pi fC}$ (reactance of a coil)

where f = frequency, cycles per second (30 to 3000) and C = (1 to 100) capacity of condenser, in microfarads.

49. $E = 0.232 \log \dfrac{d}{0.78r}$ (inductive volts per ampere per mile of line with two wires for a 25-cycle current)

where r = the radius of the wire in inches and d = the spacing in inches (4 to 100). Express r in B and S gage numbers, which vary from (0000 to 10).

50. Double-graduate the E scale of problem 49 to solve the formula, when using a 60-cycle current:

$$E = (0.232 \times 3.4) \log \dfrac{d}{0.78r}$$

Aeronautical

51. $q = \dfrac{\rho V^2}{2}$ (dynamic pressure of air moving at velocity V)

where ρ = air density slugs per cubic foot (0.0010 to 0.0025) and V = velocity of air, feet per second (30 to 300).

52. $R = \dfrac{S^2}{A}$ (aspect ratio of wing)

where S = span of airplane wing in feet (20 to 100), A = area of airplane wing in square feet, and R = aspect ratio (4 to 7).

53. Since $V_{mph} = \frac{30}{44} V_{fps}$ and 1 slug = 32.2 lb, double-graduate the ρ and V scales of problem 51 to increase the usefulness of the chart by eliminating the conversion of units.

54. $V_s = 29 \left(\dfrac{S}{C_{L_{[max]}}} \right)^{\frac{1}{2}}$ (stalling speed of an airplane in feet per second) where S = wing loading, pounds per square foot (5 to 40) and $C_{L(max)}$ = maximum lift coefficient (1.1 to 2.5).

55. $m = m_6 \dfrac{4}{3 + \dfrac{6}{R}}$ (slope of lift curve for aspect ratio, R)

where m_6 = slope dC_L/d at aspect ratio 6, range (4 to 7), and R = aspect ratio (4 to 7).

56. When the equation of problem 55 is constructed as a Z type, it is possible by the proper selection of moduli to make all scales uniform. Show how this can be done.

57. $F_b = \left[1.35 - 0.01 \dfrac{d}{t} \right] \cdot$ [ult. T.S.] (allowable stress in bending

in a chrome molybdenum steel tube)

where d/t = diameter/thickness of wall = thickness ratio (10 to 30) and ult. T.S. = ultimate tensile strength of material (90,000 to 180,000 psi).

General

58. $I = \frac{1}{2}Wr^2$ (moment of inertia of a right circular cylinder about its axis)

where W = total weight in pounds (1 to 25,000) and r = radius in inches (1 to 25).

59. $r = \sqrt{x^2 + y^2}$ (vector r whose co-ordinates are x and y)

where x varies (0 to 10), y varies (0 to 10).

60. $V = 2.467Dd^2$ (volume of a torus)

where D = larger diameter of torus (1 to 10) and d = small diameter of torus (1 to 10).

61. $I = \dfrac{bd^3}{12}$ (moment of inertia of rectangle)

where I = moment of inertia in inches^4, b = width of rectangle (2 to 16 in.), and d = depth of rectangle (4 to 24 in.).

62. $P = A(1 + R)^n$ (principal P after n compoundings of the amount A at the rate of interest, R)

Let A = \$1.00, R = interest rate in % (1 to 8), and n = number of times compounded (1 to 20).

Chemical

63. $\mu = \mu_1^n$ (specific viscosity referred to water with the same temperature of a salt solution whose normality is n)

where μ_1 is the specific viscosity of a normal solution and may be determined from Perry's *Chemical Engineers' Handbook*, p. 679 (1934), for various salt solutions and acids at 25°C, n varies (0.1 to 1.0), and μ varies (0.95 to 1.45).

64. $V = 174.24\sqrt{t + 459.6}\sqrt{H}$ (velocity of air at or near atmospheric pressure)

where V = (300 to 15,000 ft per min), t = temperature in degrees Fahrenheit— range (0° to 1000°), and H = velocity head in inches (0 to 5).

65. $V_1 = V\sqrt{\dfrac{P}{P_1}}$ (corrected velocity of problem 64 for pressures considerably above atmospheric)

where V_1 = (100 to 10,000 ft per min), V = as before, problem 64, P = (14.7 to 100 psi), and P_1 = 14.7 psi.

66. $V_2 = V_1\sqrt{\dfrac{1}{S}}$ (correction of V_1 of problem 65 for specific gravity)

where V_2 = (100 to 20,000 ft per min), V_1 = (as before), and S = (0.2 to 1.6), relative to air.

67. $P = M\left(10.82 - \dfrac{4425}{T}\right)$ (partial pressure of ammonia in atmosphere over a solution of M *gram moles* of ammonia per 1000 grams of water; T is the temperature in degrees centigrade absolute)

where P = (0 to 1000 mm), M = (0 to 100 grams), and T = (10° to 40°C). Note that the limits of P, M, and T are not given in the units to be used in the equation. Therefore revise the equation, noting that 1 atmosphere = 760 mm, molecular weight of NH_3 = 17.0, and zero degree absolute centigrade = −273°C.

Statistics

68. $\sigma_y = \sqrt{\dfrac{\Sigma y^2}{N}}$

where σ_y = standard deviation from mean (0.05 to 1000), Σy^2 = sum of deviations squared (1 to 10^6), and N = number of cases in sample (1 to 1000).

69. $\sigma_{est} = \sigma_y\sqrt{1 - r_{xy}^2}$ (standard error of estimate in predicting y scores from x)

where σ_y, standard deviation of y scores (1 to 20); r_{xy}, correlation of x and y scores (0.50 to 0.99), and σ_{est}, standard error of estimate (1 to 20).

Chapter Four

ALIGNMENT CHARTS (*Z* CHARTS) FOR THE SOLUTION OF EQUATIONS OF THE FORM
$f_1(u) = f_2(v) \cdot f_3(w)$

Suppose that the parallel scales (Figure 38), *A* and *B*, are graduated in accordance with their scale equations, $X_u = m_u f_1(u)$ and $X_v = m_v f_2(v)$, respectively. The diagonal scale for $f_3(w)$ joins $f_1(u_0)$ and $f_2(v_0)$, i.e., the zero values of the functions of *u* and *v*.

Let us suppose further that a straight line joining points u_1 and v_1 cuts

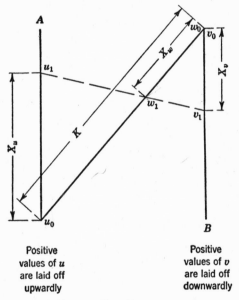

Positive values of *u* are laid off upwardly

Positive values of *v* are laid off downwardly

Fig. 38.

the diagonal scale in point w_1 so that the equation $f_1(u) = f_2(v) \cdot f_3(w)$ is satisfied. What will be the scale equation for $f_3(w)$?

From the similar triangles $u_0 u_1 w_1$ and $v_0 v_1 w_1$,

$$\frac{X_u}{X_v} = \frac{K - X_w}{X_w}$$

43

or
$$X_u = X_v \frac{(K - X_w)}{X_w}$$

since
$$X_u = m_u f_1(u)$$

and
$$X_v = m_u f_2(v)$$

Then
$$m_u f_1(u) = m_v f_2(v) \frac{(K - X_w)}{X_w}$$

If
$$f_1(u) = f_2(v) \cdot f_3(w)$$

then
$$\frac{K - X_w}{X_w} = \frac{m_u}{m_v} f_3(w)$$

from which
$$X_w = \frac{K m_v}{m_u f_3(w) + m_v}$$

or
$$X_w = \frac{K}{\dfrac{m_u}{m_v} f_3(w) + 1} = \frac{K}{K_1 f_3(w) + 1}$$

where
$$K_1 = \frac{m_u}{m_v}$$

If it is desired to graduate the w scale from u_0 instead of v_0, it can be shown that the distance from u_0 to w_1 is equal to

$$\frac{K m_u f_3(w)}{m_u f_3(w) + m_v}$$ (This should be verified by the reader.)

From the above one can construct this type of chart in the following manner:

(1) Draw scales for the variables, u and v, parallel to each other.
(2) Graduate the u scale in accordance with its scale equation, $X_u = m_u f_1(u)$.
(3) Graduate the v scale in accordance with its scale equation, $X_v = m_v f_2(v)$ (plotting positive values of v downwardly if positive values of u were plotted upwardly).
(4) Graduate the w scale from v_0 in accordance with its scale equation,

$$X_w = \frac{K}{K_1 f_3(w) + 1},$$ or from u_0 in accordance with the scale

equation, $X_w = \dfrac{K m_u f_3(w)}{m_u f_3(w) + m_v}.$

EXAMPLE 1

Consider the equation $(u + 2) = v^2w$ (Figure 39). Suppose that u varies from 0 to 10, and v from 0 to 5. The scale lengths are to be approximately 6 in.

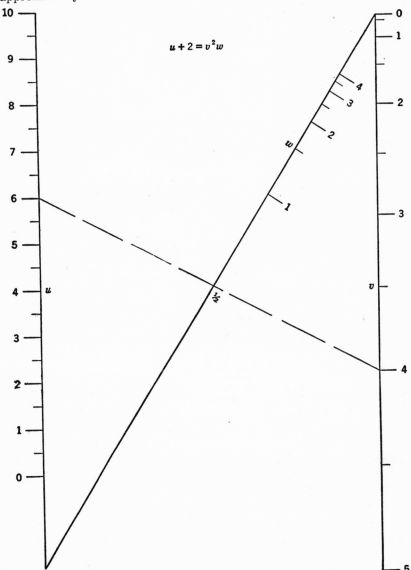

FIG. 39. Z-type Chart for the Equation, $(u + 2) = v^2w$.

$$m_u = \frac{6}{(10 + 2) - (0 + 2)} = 0.6$$

$m_v = \frac{6}{25} = 0.24.$ (We shall use 0.25, which merely lengthens the scale from 6 to 6.25 in.)

Hence, $X_u = 0.6(u + 2)$

$$X_v = 0.25v^2$$

and $$X_w = \frac{10}{\dfrac{0.6w}{0.25} + 1} = \frac{10}{\dfrac{12w}{5} + 1}$$

where $K = 10$ (ten of any convenient unit).

Form the following table:

w	0	0.5	1	2	3
X_w	10	$\frac{50}{11}$	$\frac{50}{17}$	$\frac{50}{29}$	$\frac{50}{41}$

EXAMPLE 2

Let us consider the equation for the volume of a right circular cylinder, $V = \pi r^2 h/144$, where V is the volume in cubic feet, r is the radius of the base circle, in inches (4 to 12), and h is the height of the cylinder in feet (4 to 15).   We may write the equation,

$$KV = r^2 h, \text{ where } K = \frac{144}{\pi}$$

The range of V is determined from the ranges of r and h.   Simple calculations will show that V varies from 1.40 (or $4\pi/9$) cubic feet to 47.15 (or 15π) cubic feet.

Now $$m_v = \frac{10\pm}{\dfrac{144}{\pi}\left(15\pi - \dfrac{4\pi}{9}\right)} = 0.005$$

and $$X_v = 0.005\left[\frac{144}{\pi}\left(V - \frac{4\pi}{9}\right)\right]$$

$$m_r = \frac{10\pm}{144 - 16} = 0.08$$

$$X_r = 0.08[r^2 - 4^2]$$

From the above scale equations, we can graduate the V and r scales. It will be observed that it is necessary only to compute the total length of the V scale; i.e., $X_v = 0.005 \left[\dfrac{144}{\pi} \left(15\pi - \dfrac{4\pi}{9} \right) \right] = 10.48$. Then we know that the lower point of the scale will be marked 1.40 and the upper point will be marked 47.15. Additional graduations can be obtained by proportion. Since the function is linear, the scale is uniform.

In the case of the r scale, it should be noted that the function is r^2, and therefore distances between consecutive points are proportional to the square of r.

The location of the diagonal scale must be determined next. Many students make the typical error of connecting point 4 on the r scale with point 1.40 on the V scale. Remember that the diagonal line joins the zero value of the function of r with the zero value of the function of V. These points would be zero on the r scale and zero on the V scale. In this case, it would be possible to include these points on the respective scales. However, often the zero values of the functions are not accessible within the limits of the drawing. Let us assume this to be the case in our problem.

The position of the h scale can be established by a very simple method. Let us locate points 6 and 12 on the h scale. If we let $r = 10$, then $V = 13.1$ when $h = 6$. The line joining $r = 10$ with $V = 13.1$ contains $h = 6$. Again, if we let $r = 12$, then $V = 18.9$ when $h = 6$. The line joining $r = 12$ with $V = 18.9$ contains $h = 6$. Therefore, the intersection of these two lines is $h = 6$ and, in addition, is a point on the diagonal. This method can be repeated for another point such as $h = 12$. Other points on the h scale can then be located from point 12, by properly using the scale equation,

$$X_h = \frac{K}{\dfrac{m_v}{m_r} h + 1} = \frac{K}{\dfrac{0.005}{0.08} h + 1}$$

It is evident that K must be determined. This can be done, since the distance between points 6 and 12 can be measured. Hence,

$$\frac{K}{\dfrac{0.005}{0.08} \times 6 + 1} - \frac{K}{\dfrac{0.005}{0.08} \times 12 + 1} = 2.37$$

from which $K = 15.23$.

The distances from $r = 0$, along the diagonal, can now be computed from

$$X_h = \frac{15.23}{\dfrac{0.005}{0.08}h + 1} = \frac{243.68}{h + 16}$$

h	4	5	6	7	8	9	10	11	12	13	14	15
X_h	12.18	11.59	11.07	10.58	10.13	9.73	9.36	9.01	8.70	8.40	8.12	7.86
X_h from $h = 12$	3.48	2.89	2.37	1.88	1.43	1.03	0.66	0.31	0	0.30	0.58	0.84

←————————Distances below $h = 12$————————→ |←Above $h = 12$→|

The alignment chart is shown in Figure 40.

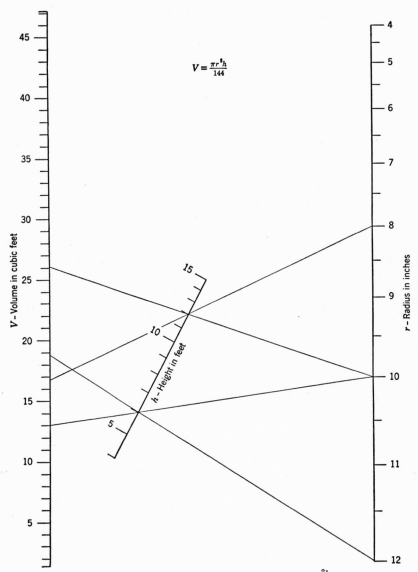

FIG. 40.   Z-type Chart for the Relation, $V = \dfrac{\pi r^2 h}{144}$.

SIMPLIFIED METHOD

A method which may simplify the work of graduating the diagonal scale can be developed in the following manner (Figure 41). Let C be

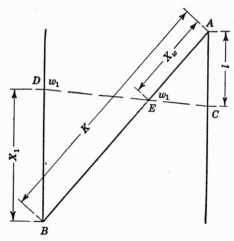

Fig. 41.

a fixed point on the right vertical scale. Let the distance from point A to the fixed point be l (inches, centimeters, or any other convenient number of units). Suppose that the *right-hand* side of the left vertical scale carries a temporary w scale. From the similar triangles, BDE and ACE,

$$\frac{X_1}{l} = \frac{K - X_w}{X_w}$$

$$X_1 = l\left[\frac{K - X_w}{X_w}\right]$$

Previously it had been shown that

$$\frac{K - X_w}{X_w} = \frac{m_u}{m_v}[f_3(w)]$$

Hence, $$X_1 = l\frac{m_u}{m_v}[f_3(w)]$$

This equation enables us to graduate the temporary w scale. Lines joining the fixed point, C, with the graduations on the temporary scale will intersect the diagonal in points having the same values of w.

This method has two advantages over the one of locating points on the diagonal from the equation,

$$X_w = \frac{K}{\dfrac{m_u}{m_v} f_3(w) + 1}$$

First, if the function of w is linear, a uniform scale can be graduated on the temporary scale; second, the length, K, of the diagonal scale need not be known.

EXAMPLE

$$B = \frac{d^2 n}{2.5} \text{ (formula taken from the Association of Automobile Manufacturing)}$$

where B represents brake horsepower, d (0 to 5 in.) the diameter of the cylinder in inches, and n (2, 4, 6, 8, 10, 12) the number of cylinders. The maximum value of $B = 120$. Suppose that the lengths of the parallel scales, B and d, are 7.5 in. The scale equations will be:

$$X_B = m_B(2.5B); \quad 7.5 = m_B(300); \quad m_B = \frac{7.5}{300} = 0.025$$

$$X_d = m_d(d^2); \quad 7.5 = m_d(25); \quad m_d = \frac{7.5}{25} = 0.3$$

(a) Applying the first method, $K = 9$ in., we have

$$X_n = \frac{9}{\dfrac{0.025}{0.3} n + 1} = \frac{9}{\dfrac{n}{12} + 1} = \frac{108}{n + 12}$$

Form the following table. (Plot n from these values.)

n	2	4	6	8	10	12
X_n	7.71	6.75	6.00	5.40	4.91	4.50

(b) Applying the second method, we obtain

$$X_1 = l\frac{m_B}{m_d} \cdot n; \quad X_1 = 5 \times \frac{0.025}{0.3} n = \frac{5n}{12}$$

Points on temporary scale $X_1 = \frac{5}{12}n$ are located on the right-hand side of the B scale. These points are connected with the fixed point, C. The intersection of these lines with the diagonal locate the points on the n scale. In this example, $l = 5$ in. (See Figure 42 for completed chart.)

EXERCISES

Since most of the problems of the "three parallel scales" type also fall in the Z type, construct Z-type charts for: Problems 22 to 29, inclusive; 31 to 45, inclusive; 47; 50 to 57, inclusive; 60 to 65, inclusive; 68 and 69.

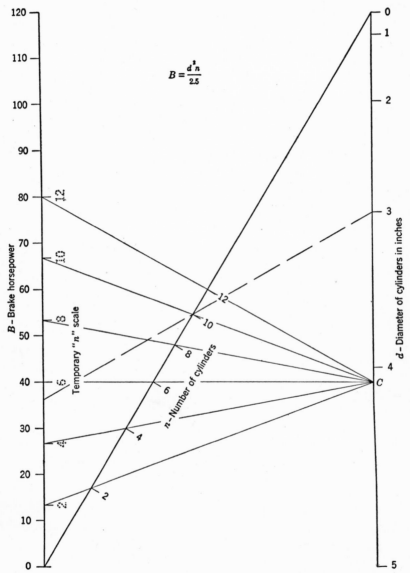

FIG. 42. Z-type Chart, Employing the Simplified Method, for the Expression,

$$B = \frac{d^2 n}{2.5}.$$

Chapter Five

OTHER FORMS OF EQUATIONS WHICH CAN BE SOLVED BY A Z CHART

$$f_1(u) + f_2(v) = \frac{f_1(u)}{f_3(w)}$$

Let us consider Figure 43, which shows the v scale on the left, graduated in accordance with the scale equation $X_v = m_v f_2(v)$ and the u scale on the right, graduated from the scale equation, $X_u = m_u f_1(u)$. Note that positive values of the variable, v, are plotted upwardly, and that

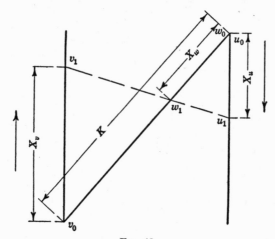

FIG. 43.

positive values of the variable, u, are plotted downwardly. The diagonal scale which carries the graduations for the function of w joins the zero values of the functions of u and v.

What is the scale equation for the function of w, in order to have co-linear points on the u, v, and w scales satisfy the given equation

$$f_1(u) + f_2(v) = \frac{f_1(u)}{f_3(w)}$$

54

From the similar triangles $v_0 v_1 w_1$ and $u_0 u_1 w_1$ it follows that

$$\frac{X_v}{X_u} = \frac{K - X_w}{X_w}$$

If
$$X_u = m_u f_1(u)$$
$$X_v = m_v f_2(v)$$

and
$$X_w = m_w f_3(w)$$

then
$$\frac{m_v f_2(v)}{m_u f_1(u)} = \frac{K - m_w f_3(w)}{m_w f_3(w)}$$

or
$$\frac{m_u f_1(u) + m_v f_2(v)}{m_u f_1(u)} = \frac{K}{m_w f_3(w)}$$

and
$$m_u f_1(u) + m_v f_2(v) = \frac{K m_u f_1(u)}{m_w f_3(w)}$$

If
$$K = m_w \quad \text{and} \quad m_u = m_v$$

then
$$f_1(u) + f_2(v) = \frac{f_1(u)}{f_2(w)}$$

Therefore to construct a chart of this form, graduate the scales in accordance with the scale equations:

$$X_u = m_u f_1(u)$$
$$X_v = m_u f_2(v)$$
$$X_w = K f_3(w)$$

EXAMPLE

$$f = \frac{20,000}{1 + \dfrac{144 L^2}{9000 r^2}}$$

(Gordon Column Formula)

L (0 to 50 ft)

r (0 to 10 in.)

This equation can be reduced to the form

$$r^2 + 0.016 L^2 = \frac{r^2}{\dfrac{f}{20,000}}$$

The equation is the same form as the type which was developed above.

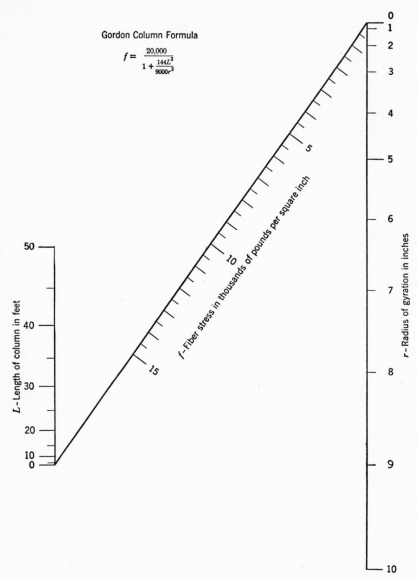

Fig. 44.   Gordon Column Formula.

The scale equations are:

$$X_r = m_r r^2$$
$$X_L = m_r (0.016L^2)$$

(Remember that the moduli for the parallel scales are the same.)

$$X_f = K \left(\frac{f}{20,000}\right)$$

If the length of the r scale is 7.5 in., then

$$m_r = \frac{7.5}{(10)^2} = 0.075$$

or $\qquad X_r = 0.075r^2$

Now $\qquad X_L = 0.075(0.016L^2) = 0.0012L^2$

If we let $\qquad K = 8$

then $\qquad X_f = 8\left(\frac{f}{20,000}\right) = 0.0004f$

The chart is shown in Figure 44.

If the equation is of the form,

$$f_1(u) - f_2(v) = \frac{f_1(u)}{f_3(w)}$$

the scales for u and v will be graduated in the same direction as shown below (Figure 45).

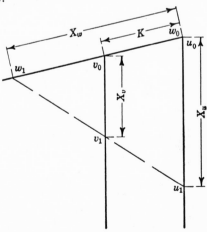

Fig. 45.

EXERCISES

70. Bazin coefficient for velocity in open channel flow:

$$C = \frac{87}{0.552 + \dfrac{m}{\sqrt{R}}}$$

where m = coefficient of roughness (0.06 to 2) and R = hydraulic radius in feet (0.2 to 25).

71. $\text{S.G.} = \dfrac{W}{W - W'}$ (specific gravity of a body)

where W = weight in air (0 to 10), W' = weight in water (0 to 10), and S.G. varies (1 to 15).

72. $\left(\dfrac{d}{t}\right) = \dfrac{2f - P}{P}; \left[\left(\dfrac{d}{t}\right) \text{ required for a thick-walled tube subjected to} \right.$ internal pressure where $\dfrac{d}{t}$ is more than $4 \Big]$

where f = maximum fiber stress of material (5000 to 60,000 psi), P = internal pressure (1000 to 10,000 psi), and (d/t) varies from 4 to 12.

Chapter Six

ALIGNMENT CHARTS FOR THE SOLUTION OF EQUATIONS OF THE FORM

$$\frac{1}{f_1(u)} + \frac{1}{f_2(v)} = \frac{1}{f_3(w)}$$

Suppose that the intersecting scales, A and C, are graduated in accordance with the scale equations (Figure 46):

$$X_u = m_u f_1(u)$$

$$X_v = m_v f_2(v)$$

If a straight line joining points u_1 and v_1 intersects scale B in a point

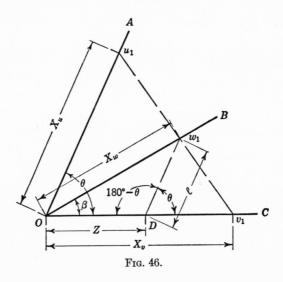

Fig. 46.

w_1 so that the given equation is satisfied, how should the w scale be graduated and how is it located?

59

Through w_1 let us draw a line parallel to scale A. From the similar triangles Ou_1v_1 and Dw_1v_1,

$$\frac{X_v}{X_u} = \frac{X_v - Z}{\ell}$$

$$X_v\ell = X_uX_v - X_uZ$$

$$\frac{1}{X_u} = \frac{1}{\ell} - \frac{Z}{X_v\ell}$$

$$\frac{1}{m_uf_1(u)} + \frac{Z}{m_vf_2(v)\cdot\ell} = \frac{1}{\ell}$$

$$\frac{1}{f_1(u)} + \frac{Zm_u}{m_vf_2(v)\ell} = \frac{m_u}{\ell}$$

In order that the second term of the left-hand member shall become $1/f_2(v)$,

let

$$\frac{Z}{\ell} = \frac{m_v}{m_u}$$

from which

$$\ell = \frac{Zm_u}{m_v}$$

Hence,

$$\frac{1}{f_1(u)} + \frac{1}{f_2(v)} = \frac{m_v}{Z}$$

If

$$Z = m_vf_3(w)$$

then

$$\frac{1}{f_1(u)} + \frac{1}{f_2(v)} = \frac{1}{f_3(w)}$$

Therefore, to construct a chart of the above form:

(*a*) Graduate the scales for $f_1(u)$ and $f_2(v)$ in accordance with their scale equations, $X_u = m_uf_1(u)$ and $X_v = m_vf_2(v)$, respectively.

(*b*) Locate the scale for $f_3(w)$ so that

$$\frac{Z}{\ell} = \frac{m_v}{m_u}$$

(*c*) Graduate the *C*-scale (see Figure 46) with a temporary w scale, using the scale equation, $Z = m_vf_3(w)$, and project the points of this scale onto the w scale by means of parallels to the scale A.

ALTERNATE METHOD

A method for graduating the w scale directly can be developed in the following manner:

By trigonometry,

$$X_w{}^2 = Z^2 + \ell^2 - 2Z\ell \cos (180° - \theta)$$

$$= Z^2 + \left(Z \frac{m_u}{m_v} \right)^2 - 2Z^2 \left(\frac{m_u}{m_v} \right)(- \cos \theta)$$

$$= Z^2 \left[1 + \left(\frac{m_u}{m_v} \right)^2 + 2 \left(\frac{m_u}{m_v} \right) \cos \theta \right]$$

$$= \left[m_v{}^2 \cdot f_3(w)^2 \right] \left[1 + \frac{m_u{}^2}{m_v{}^2} + 2 \frac{m_u}{m_v} \cos \theta \right]$$

$$= [m_v{}^2 + m_u{}^2 + 2m_u m_v \cos \theta] f_3(w)$$

$$X_w = [m_v{}^2 + m_u{}^2 + 2m_u m_v \cos \theta]^{\frac{1}{2}} f_3(w)$$

Then let $X_w = m_w f_3(w)$

Therefore $m_w = [m_v{}^2 + m_u{}^2 + 2m_u m_v \cos \theta]^{\frac{1}{2}}$

The w scale can be located by the relation

$$\frac{Z}{\ell} = \frac{m_v}{m_u}$$

EXAMPLE

$$\frac{1}{u} + \frac{1}{v} = \frac{1}{f} \quad \text{(lens formula) (Figure 47)}$$

where u = object distance (0 to 100), v = image distance (0 to 80), f = focal distance (0 to 50).

The scale equations are:

$$X_u = m_u(u); \quad m_u = \tfrac{6}{100}; \quad X_u = 0.06u$$

where the length of the u scale is 6 in.

$$X_v = m_v(v); \quad m_v = \tfrac{4}{80}; \quad X_v = 0.05v$$

where the length of the v scale is 4 in.

Let $\qquad \theta = 60°$

$$m_f = (m_v{}^2 + m_u{}^2 + 2m_u m_v \cos \theta)^{\frac{1}{2}}$$

$$= (0.06^2 + 0.05^2 + 2 \times 0.06 \times 0.05 \times 0.5)^{\frac{1}{2}}$$

$$= (0.0036 + 0.0025 + 0.003)^{\frac{1}{2}}$$

$$= 0.0955$$

$$X_f = 0.0955f$$

$$\frac{Z}{\ell} = \frac{0.05}{0.06} = \frac{5}{6} \quad \left(\text{Recall that } \frac{Z}{\ell} = \frac{m_v}{m_u}. \right)$$

Only one point, such as point 50, need be located on the f scale from the scale equation $X_f = 0.0955f$. The other points may be projected geometrically. The same is true of the u and v scales.

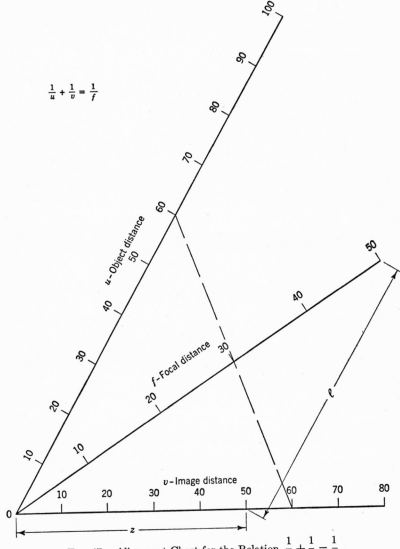

$$\frac{1}{u} + \frac{1}{v} = \frac{1}{f}$$

FIG. 47.   Alignment Chart for the Relation, $\dfrac{1}{u} + \dfrac{1}{v} = \dfrac{1}{f}$.

SPECIAL CASE 1

If $m_v = m_u$ and $\theta = 120°$,

$$X_w = m_w f_3(w) = m_u f_3(w)$$

$$\frac{Z}{\ell} = \frac{m_v}{m_u} = 1$$

It can be shown easily by geometry that whenever

$$\frac{Z}{\ell} = 1$$

the w scale bisects the angle θ; that is, $\beta = \theta/2$ (see Figure 48).

$$m_w = [m_u{}^2 + m_u{}^2 + 2m_u{}^2(-\tfrac{1}{2})]^{\frac{1}{2}}$$

$$= m_u$$

Hence the three scales would have the same modulus.

EXAMPLE

$$\frac{1}{r_1} + \frac{1}{r_2} = \frac{1}{r} \text{ (Figure 48)}$$

Let r_1 and r_2 vary from 0 to 10 ohms, and r from 0 to 5 ohms. If the scale lengths for r_1 and r_2 are $2\frac{1}{2}$ in., then

$$m_{r_1} = \frac{2.5}{10} = 0.25$$

$$m_{r_2} = m_{r_1} = 0.25$$

Therefore, the scale equations are:

$$X_{r_1} = 0.25r_1 \quad \text{and} \quad X_{r_2} = 0.25r_2$$

Since the angle between the scales is 120°, $m_r = m_{r_1} = 0.25$. Thus the scale equation for the r scale is $X_r = 0.25r$. Again, since $m_{r_2} = m_{r_1}$, the r scale bisects the angle between the r_1 and r_2 scales. The completed chart is shown in Figure 48.

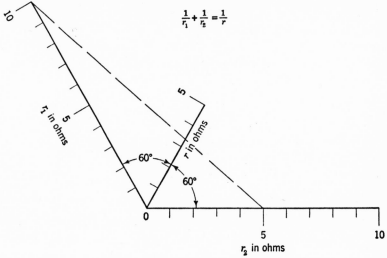

$$\frac{1}{r_1} + \frac{1}{r_2} = \frac{1}{r}$$

FIG. 48.   Alignment Chart for the Equation, $\dfrac{1}{r_1} + \dfrac{1}{r_2} = \dfrac{1}{r}$.

SPECIAL CASE 2

If $\theta = 90°$, we have

$$m_w = [m_u{}^2 + m_v{}^2 + 2m_u m_v \cos 90°]^{\frac{1}{2}}$$

$$m_w = [m_u{}^2 + m_v{}^2]^{\frac{1}{2}}$$

$$\frac{Z}{\ell} = \frac{m_v}{m_u} = \cot \beta$$

$$\beta = \cot^{-1}\left(\frac{m_v}{m_u}\right)$$

EXAMPLE

$$\frac{1}{R_1} + \frac{1}{R_2} = \frac{1}{R} \quad \text{(Figure 49)}$$

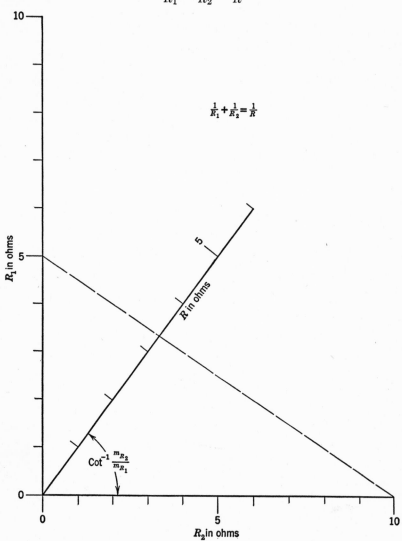

$\frac{1}{R_1} + \frac{1}{R_2} = \frac{1}{R}$

FIG. 49.   Alignment Chart for the Equation, $\dfrac{1}{R_1} + \dfrac{1}{R_2} = \dfrac{1}{R}$.   Two Scales at Right Angles.

Let R_1 and R_2 vary from 0 to 10 ohms, and R from 0 to 5 ohms. Suppose that the R_1 scale is 4 in. long; that the R_2 scale is 3 in. long; and that the angle between the scales is 90°. Now

$$m_{R_1} = \tfrac{4}{10} = 0.4$$

$$X_{R_1} = 0.4R_1$$

Furthermore,

$$m_{R_2} = \tfrac{3}{10} = 0.3$$

and

$$X_{R_2} = 0.3R_2$$

From the above, it follows that

$$m_R = [0.4^2 + 0.3^2]^{1/2} = 0.5$$

Therefore

$$X_R = 0.5R$$

The R-scale is located by the ratio $m_{R_2}/m_{R_1} = 0.3/0.4$.

EXERCISES

73.
$$\frac{1}{u^2} + \frac{2}{v} = \frac{1}{w^3}$$

where u varies 0 to 5 and v varies 0 to 10.

74.
$$\frac{1}{u} + \frac{3}{v^2} = \frac{1}{w}$$

where u varies 0 to 10 and v varies 0 to 8.

Chapter Seven

ALIGNMENT CHARTS FOR EQUATIONS OF FOUR OR MORE VARIABLES OF THE FORM

$$f_1(u) + f_2(v) + f_3(w) \cdots = f_4(q)$$

EXAMPLE 1

Let us consider the relation

$$u + 2v + 3w = 4t$$

Let $$u + 2v = Q \qquad (1)$$

then $$Q + 3w = 4t \qquad (2)$$

These two equations are of the form discussed in Chapter Three.
Suppose (equation 1) that $m_u = 1$; $m_v = \frac{1}{2}$; then

$$X_u = u \quad \text{and} \quad X_v = \tfrac{1}{2}(2v) = v$$

Now $$\frac{m_u}{m_v} = \frac{1}{\frac{1}{2}} = \frac{2}{1}; \quad m_Q = \frac{1 \times \frac{1}{2}}{1 + \frac{1}{2}} = \frac{1}{3}$$

If (equation 2) $m_w = \frac{1}{3}$; $X_w = \frac{1}{3}(3w) = w$

$$\frac{m_Q}{m_w} = \frac{\frac{1}{3}}{\frac{1}{3}} = \frac{1}{1}; \quad m_t = \frac{\frac{1}{3} \times \frac{1}{3}}{\frac{1}{3} + \frac{1}{3}} = \frac{\frac{1}{9}}{\frac{2}{3}} = \frac{1}{6}$$

Therefore $$X_t = \tfrac{1}{6}(4t) = \tfrac{2}{3}t$$

From the above calculations, we may now proceed to construct the chart (Figure 50).

Now consider *equation 1*, $u + 2v = Q$. Scales u and v are placed a convenient distance apart. Scale u is graduated from its scale equation, $X_u = u$; and scale v is graduated from its scale equation, $X_v = \frac{1}{2}(2v) = v$. The Q scale is located in accordance with the ratio, $m_u/m_v = 1/\frac{1}{2} = 2/1$. This scale is *not* graduated.

Now consider *equation 2*, $Q + 3w = 4t$. Scale w is placed a convenient distance from the Q scale. Graduations on the w scale are located in accordance with its scale equation, $X_w = \frac{1}{3}(3w) = w$. The t scale is located from the ratio, $m_Q/m_w = \frac{1}{3}/\frac{1}{3} = 1/1$. The t scale is then graduated from the scale equation, $X_t = \frac{1}{6}(4t) = \frac{2}{3}t$.

It should be carefully noted that in most of the practical applications of this form, it is necessary to locate a point on the fourth scale (by a

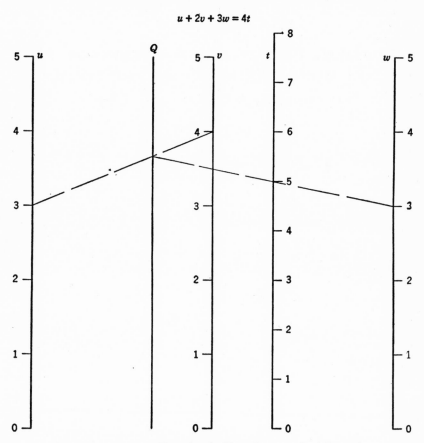

Fig. 50.   Alignment Chart for the Equation, $u + 2v + 3w = 4t$.

computation from the given equation) before graduating that scale. The chart is shown in Figure 50.

EXAMPLE 2

$$R = 19.64Cd^2\sqrt{h}$$

where R = rate of flow through an orifice, in gallons per minute; C = orifice coefficient (0.6 to 1.6); d = orifice diameter (0.1 to 1.0 in.), and h = head (10 to 100 ft).

Our first step is to write the given equation in type form:

Case a:

$$\log R - \log 19.64 = \log C + 2 \log d + \tfrac{1}{2} \log h$$

Let
$$\log C + 2 \log d = T \tag{1}$$

and
$$\log R - \log 19.64 = T + \tfrac{1}{2} \log h \tag{2}$$

Equations 1 and 2 are now of the form $f_1(u) + f_2(v) = f_3(w)$. The nomogram would look like Figure 51.

With this arrangement of scales, it will be observed that the operation of the chart would require, first, a line (isopleth) joining points on

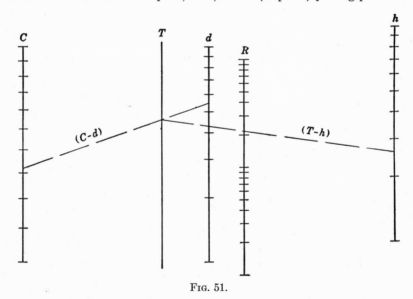

Fɪɢ. 51.

the C and d scales. The intersection of this line with the T scale (dummy or turning axis) would then be joined with a point on the h scale. The intersection of the latter line with the R scale would give the result.

Now let us try a different analysis of the problem. Suppose we write the equations:

Case b:

$$\log C + 2 \log d = T$$

and $$\log R - \log 19.64 - \tfrac{1}{2} \log h = T$$

Now the arrangement of scales would look like Figure 52. *Note*: Graduations on the h scale will be directed downwardly, since a minus sign precedes $\tfrac{1}{2} \log h$.

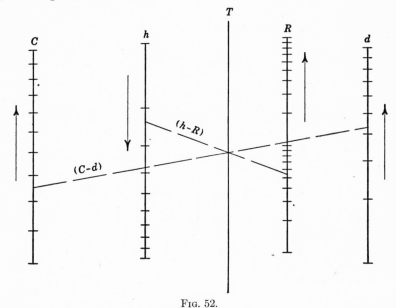

Fig. 52.

Case c:

A third analysis of the given equation shows that we could write:

$$\log R - \log 19.64 = T + \tfrac{1}{2} \log h$$

and $$T - \log C = 2 \log d$$

The arrangement of scales in this case would look like Figure 53. Note that this arrangement is much better than the first two, since there is greater clarity in operation and reading.

Having completed the preliminary studies, let us now make the

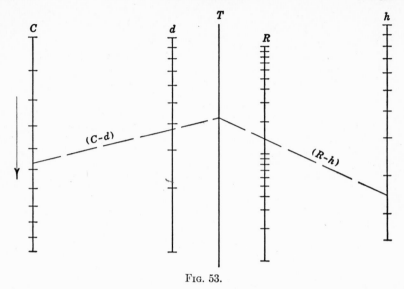

Fig. 53.

necessary computations for the final design of the chart which is shown above.   Consider equation $T - \log C = 2 \log d$.

For scale C

$$m_C = \frac{X_C}{[\log C_n - \log C_0]} = \frac{4 \text{ in. } \pm}{\log 1.6 - \log 0.6} = 9.4 \text{ (use 10.0)}$$

or $X_C = 10[\log C - \log 0.6]$, scale equation for C

For scale d

$$m_d = \frac{4 \text{ in. } \pm}{2 \log 1.0 - 2 \log 0.1} = 2$$

$$X_d = 2[2 \log d - 2 \log 0.1], \text{ scale equation for } d$$

Now $$m_d = \frac{m_C \cdot m_T}{m_C + m_T}$$

or $$2 = \frac{10 m_T}{10 + m_T}$$

$$m_T = 2.5; \quad \frac{m_C}{m_T} = \frac{10}{2.5} = \frac{4}{1}$$

Sketch layout for $T - \log C = 2 \log d$ is shown in Figure 54. Now let us consider the equation

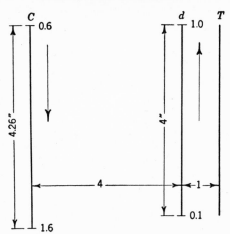

FIG. 54.

$$\log R - \log 19.64 = T + \tfrac{1}{2} \log h$$

For scale h

$$m_h = \frac{7.5 \text{ in.}}{\tfrac{1}{2} \log 100 - \tfrac{1}{2} \log 10} = 15$$

or

$$X_h = 15[\tfrac{1}{2} \log h - \tfrac{1}{2} \log 10] = 7.5[\log h - \log 10]$$

$$\frac{m_T}{m_h} = \frac{2.5}{15} = \frac{1}{6}$$

The modulus for the R scale is

$$m_R = \frac{m_T \cdot m_h}{m_T + m_h} = \frac{2.5 \times 15}{2.5 + 15} = 2.14$$

and

$$X_R = 2.14[\log R - \log R_1]$$

where R_1 is a point on the R scale. This point is computed from the original equation.

The sketch layout for $\log R - \log 19.64 = T + \frac{1}{2} \log h$ is shown in Figure 55.   The completed chart is shown in Figure 56.

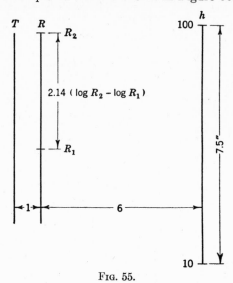

FIG. 55.

The designer is cautioned to check the positioning of the R scale in each case, before the adoption of the final form.   In some cases, it will be found that the most desirable form, case c in the above example, may yield one scale whose graduations are not properly oriented with respect to the other scales, that is, one scale may be practically out of reach in spite of the fact that the "length" of the graduated scale is satisfactory.

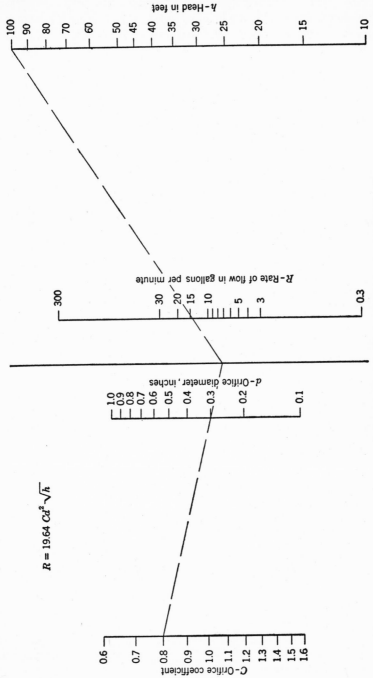

Fig. 56. Alignment Chart for the Expression, $R = 19.64Cd^2\sqrt{h}$.

Chapter Eight

PROPORTIONAL CHARTS OF THE FORM

$$\frac{f_1(u)}{f_2(v)} = \frac{f_3(w)}{f_4(q)}$$

This equation can be solved in a manner similar to that used in the preceding problem. This simply means transforming the above equation to the form

$$\log f_1(u) - \log f_2(v) = \log f_3(w) - \log f_4(q)$$

In many cases, however, where the functions are linear, the proportional type alignment chart has a distinct advantage in that the scales

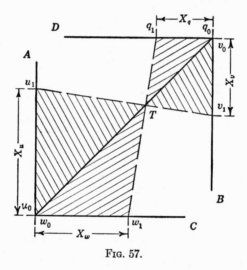

Fig. 57.

are uniform, thus permitting more accurate readings and also simplifying the construction of the scales.

Consider the figure shown in Figure 57.

Scales A and B are parallel to each other, and graduated in accordance with the scale equations:

$$X_u = m_u f_1(u) \quad \text{and} \quad X_v = m_v f_2(v), \text{ respectively}$$

In a similar manner, scales C and D are parallel to each other, and are graduated in accordance with the scale equations:

$$X_w = m_w f_3(w) \quad \text{and} \quad X_q = m_q f_4(q)$$

The angle between scales A and C may be of any convenient magnitude. Triangles $u_1 u_0 T$ and $v_1 v_0 T$ are similar, hence

$$\frac{X_u}{X_v} = \frac{u_0 T}{v_0 T}$$

Likewise, triangles $w_0 T w_1$ and $q_0 T q_1$ are similar, hence

$$\frac{X_w}{X_q} = \frac{w_0 T}{q_0 T}$$

But lengths $u_0 T = w_0 T$; and $v_0 T = q_0 T$. Therefore

$$\frac{X_u}{X_v} = \frac{X_w}{X_q}$$

or
$$\frac{m_u f_1(u)}{m_v f_2(v)} = \frac{m_w f_3(w)}{m_q f_4(q)}$$

Since
$$\frac{f_1(u)}{f_2(v)} = \frac{f_3(w)}{f_4(q)}$$

it follows that
$$\frac{m_u}{m_v} = \frac{m_w}{m_q}$$

This means that three moduli may be determined from the given data, but the fourth modulus will be dependent upon the first three.

EXAMPLE 1 (Figure 58)

$$t = \frac{Pd}{2f}$$ (thickness of a pipe to withstand internal pressures, where $P =$ pressure (25 to 100 psi)

where f = allowable stress (3000 to 15,000 psi), d = diameter of pipe (10 to 60 in.), and t = thickness of pipe ($\frac{1}{8}$ to $\frac{1}{2}$ in.). The given equation may be put in type form by writing $\dfrac{t}{d} = \dfrac{P}{2f}$.

$$t = \frac{Pd}{2f}$$

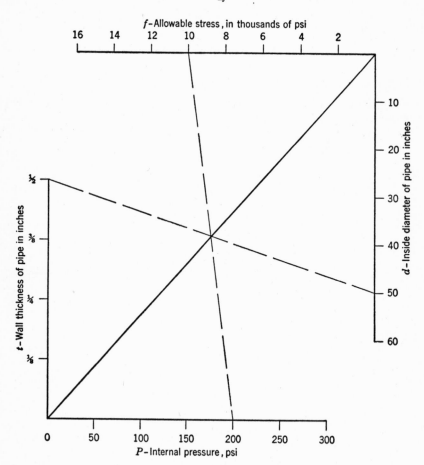

FIG. 58.   Proportional Type Chart for the Relation, $t = \dfrac{Pd}{2f}$.

Now
$$m_t = \frac{5 \text{ in.}}{\frac{1}{2}} = 10 \text{ in.}$$

and
$$X_t = 10t \text{ (scale equation for } t\text{)}$$

$$m_d = \frac{5 \text{ in.} \pm}{60} = 0.0833 \text{ (use 0.1)}$$

and
$$X_d = 0.1d \text{ (scale equation for } d\text{)}$$

$$m_f = \frac{5 \text{ in.} \pm}{30,000} = 0.000166 \text{ (use 0.0002)}$$

and
$$X_f = 0.0002(2f) = 0.0004f$$

The modulus for P is now computed from $m_t/m_d = m_p/m_f$; or $10/0.1 = m_p/0.0002$; $m_P = 0.02$ and $X_P = 0.02P$. (See Figure 58 for completed chart.)

EXAMPLE 2

$$E = 15(V - v)\left(1 + \frac{w}{10}\right) \text{ (Meyer's evaporation formula) (Figure 59)}$$

where E = the evaporation in inches per month (0 to 10); V = saturated vapor pressure corresponding to monthly mean temperature, t, degrees Fahrenheit, which varies from 30° to 90°; v = the actual vapor pressure; w = the monthly mean wind velocity, mph (0 to 30).

Since

$$v = V \times \text{R.H.}$$

where R.H. = the monthly mean relative humidity (30% to 90%) and $E = 15V(1 - \text{R.H.})(1 + w/10)$.

Or
$$\frac{E}{10 + w} = \frac{1.5(1 - \text{R.H.})}{\dfrac{1}{f(t)}}$$

where V is a function of t.

$$m_E = \frac{6.25}{10} = \frac{5}{8}; \quad X_E = \frac{5}{8}E$$

Range of $f(t)$ is 0.164 to 1.408.

$$m_t = \frac{4\frac{1}{2}}{\dfrac{1}{0.164}} = 0.738 \text{ (use 0.75)}; \quad X_t = 0.75\frac{1}{f(t)}$$

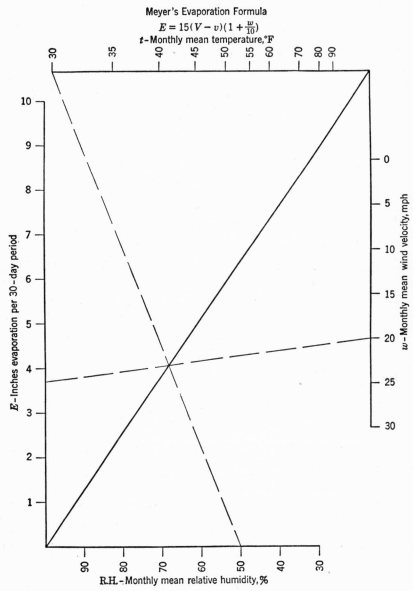

FIG. 59.   Meyer's Evaporation Formula, $E = 15(V - v)\left(1 + \dfrac{w}{10}\right)$.

$$m_w = \frac{5}{10 + 30} = \frac{1}{8}; \quad X_w = \frac{1}{8}(10 + w)$$

$$\frac{\frac{5}{8}}{\frac{1}{8}} = \frac{m_{\text{R.H.}}}{0.75}$$

Therefore $m_{\text{R.H.}} = \frac{15}{4}$; $X_{\text{R.H.}} = \frac{15}{4} \times 1.5(1 - \text{R.H.}) = \frac{90}{16}(1 - \text{R.H.})$

$$= \frac{45}{8}(1 - \text{R.H.})$$

The angle between scales A and C (or D and B) need not be 90°. In fact, scale C could coincide with scale A, which means that scale D

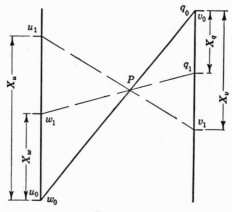

FIG. 60.

would coincide with scale B. A study of Figure 60 will reveal that the above statement is true.

$$\frac{X_u}{X_v} = \frac{u_0P}{Pv_0}$$

$$\frac{X_w}{X_q} = \frac{w_0P}{Pq_0}$$

and since $u_0 \equiv w_0$ and $v_0 \equiv q_0$,

$$\frac{X_u}{X_v} = \frac{X_w}{X_q}$$

Hence, if

$$X_u = m_u f_1(u)$$

$$X_v = m_v f_2(v)$$

$$X_w = m_w f_3(w)$$

$$X_q = m_q f_4(q)$$

and

$$\frac{m_u}{m_v} = \frac{m_w}{m_q}$$

then

$$\frac{f_1(u)}{f_2(v)} = \frac{f_3(w)}{f_4(q)}$$

Variations of the above charts are shown in Figures 61, 62, and 63.

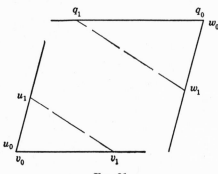

FIG. 61.

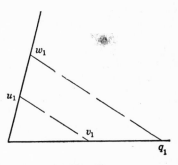

FIG. 62.

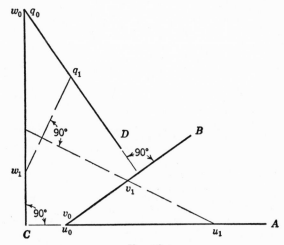

FIG. 63.

EXERCISES

Hydraulics

75. $t = \dfrac{Pd}{2f}$ (required thickness of a pipe to withstand an internal pressure)

where t = thickness in inches (0 to $\frac{1}{4}$); P = internal pressure, pounds per square inch (0 to 100); f = allowable stress, pounds per square inch (0 to 15,000); d = diameter of pipe in inches (0 to 60).

76. $R = \dfrac{\rho v l}{\mu}$ (Reynolds number as used for fluid motion [0 to 1,000,000])

where v = velocity, feet per second (0 to 10); l = characteristic dimension (0 to 2 ft); μ = coefficient of viscosity, and for water is a function of temperature given by the following table·

T	μ
32°F	374×10^{-7}
50	273×10^{-7}
68	211×10^{-7}
86	167×10^{-7}
104	137×10^{-7}
122	115×10^{-7}
140	97.8×10^{-7}
158	84.6×10^{-7}
176	74.4×10^{-7}
194	66.1×10^{-7}
212	59.2×10^{-7}

$$\rho = \frac{62.4}{32.2} \text{ (for water)}$$

77. $Q = C_d a \sqrt{2gh}$ (discharge from an orifice or nozzle in cubic feet per second [0 to 20])

where c_d = coefficient of discharge (0.5 to 1.0); a = area of the orifice (0 to 1.0 sq ft); h = head of water on the orifice (0 to 20 ft); g = 32.2

78. $v = \dfrac{1.486}{n} R^{\frac{2}{3}} S^{\frac{1}{2}}$ (velocity in an open channel (0 to 30 ft per second) [Manning's formula])

where n = coefficient of roughness (0.009 to 0.035); R = hydraulic radius (0 to 20 ft); S = slope of channel (0 to 0.01).

79. $V = C\sqrt{RS}$ (Chezy formula for velocity in an open channel)

Use same limits as in problem 78.

80. $\dfrac{N_s}{N} = \sqrt{\dfrac{\text{HP}}{H^{5/4}}}$ (formula for a reaction turbine)

where N_s = specific speed (10 to 100); N = speed in rpm (100 to 2000); HP = horsepower (to 1000); H = head of water (10 to 200 ft).

Strength of Materials

81. $f = \dfrac{6M}{bH^2}$ (Stress in the outer fiber of a section of a rectangular beam)

where M = bending moment on the section in inch-pounds (10,000 to 300,000); b = breadth of section, inches (2 to 16); h = depth of section, inches (3 to 20); f = fiber stress, pounds per square inch (750 to 1300).

82. $f = \dfrac{Mc}{I}$ (fiber stress in a beam of any cross section)

where f = fiber stress, pounds per square inch (3000 to 15,000); M = bending moment on section in inch-pounds (25,000 to 300,000); c = distance from neutral axis where stress is to be found (0 to 10 in.); I = moment of inertia of section (100 to 10,000 in.^{4}).

83. $P = 0.196\,\dfrac{d^3}{r}\,f$ (load supported by a helical compression spring)

where d = diameter of wire corresponding to B. & S. gage numbers (0000 to 10); r = mean radius of spring (0.5 to 2 in.); f = shearing stress of material (10,000 to 60,000 psi).

84. $d = 68.5\sqrt[3]{\dfrac{H}{n(T_{\max})}}$ (required diameter of a shaft in torsion)

where H = horsepower to be transmitted—varies from (0 to 500 hp); n = speed of rotation, rpm (0 to 4000); $T_{\max}$ = working stress in shear, pounds per square inch (5000 to 15,000); d = diameter (0 to 3 in.).

85. Euler's column formula: $\dfrac{P}{A} = \dfrac{C\pi^2 E}{\left(\dfrac{L}{\rho}\right)^2}$

where P/A = critical average stress in pounds per square inch, varies from (500 to 20,000); C = fixity coefficient (1 to 4); E = modulus of elasticity (1 to 30 million psi); L/ρ = radius of gyration (70 to 200).

Civil

86. $X = \dfrac{l^3}{6R_c L_c}$ (offset from the tangent in a spiral easement curve, range 0 to 75)

where l = distance in feet from T.S. (point of spiral), range (0 to 600); R_c = radius of circle in feet (300 to 6000); L_c = total length of spiral in feet (0 to 600).

87. $S = \dfrac{l^2}{2R_cL_c}$ (the "spiral angle" or total inclination of curve to tangent at any point on a spiral easement curve, range, 0° to 30°)

where l = distance in feet from T.S. (point of spiral), range (0 to 600); R_c = radius of circle in feet (300 to 6000); L_c = total length of spiral in feet (0 to 600).

88. Since $D = \dfrac{5729.65}{R_c}$ (double-graduate the R_c scale in problem 86 or 87 to read D, range 1° to 20°)

89. $e = \dfrac{gv^2}{32.2R}$ (elevation of track in feet)

where g = gauge of track; v = velocity in feet per second (0 to 60); R = radius of curve in feet (300 to 6000).

90. $C_s = \dfrac{W^2L^3}{24P^2}$ (correction to a steel tape due to sag [0 to 0.5])

where W = weight of tape in pounds per foot (0 to 0.04); L = length of tape between supports (0 to 100 ft); P = applied tension in pounds (0 to 10).

91. $E = 15[V - v]\left[1 + \dfrac{w}{10}\right]$ (Meyer's evaporation formula)

where E is the evaporation in inches per 30-day month (0 to 15 in.).

Make the substitution for $v = $ (R.H.) V, where v is the actual vapor pressure, R.H. the relative humidity, and V the vapor pressure at 100% R.H. and is a function of temperature as given in problem 10, functional scales. W is the average wind velocity in miles per hour, varying from (0 to 30) and R.H. is (30% to 90%).

Mechanical

92. $HP = \dfrac{2\pi LNW}{33,000}$ (horsepower as measured by a prony brake [HP, 0 to 75])

where L = length of brake arm in feet (0.5 to 1.5); N = shaft speed, revolutions per minute (0 to 4000); W = load on scales (0 to 200 lb).

93. $\dfrac{P_1}{P_2} = \left[\dfrac{V_2}{V_1}\right]^{1.41}$ (adiabatic expansion of air)

where P_1 = initial pressure (0 to 300 psi); P_2 = final pressure (0 to 275 psi); V_1 = initial volume (0 to 100 cu ft); V_2 = final volume (0 to 110 cu ft).

94. $M = 0.3155A_t \sqrt{\dfrac{P_1}{V_1}}$ (discharge from a steam nozzle in a turbine in pounds per second [0 to 6])

where A_t = exit area of nozzle in square inches (0 to 5); P_1 = pressure of steam (15 to 300 psi); V_1 = specific volume, cubic feet per pound (0 to 26).

95. $W = \dfrac{D \times H^2 \times F}{B}$ (minimum weight of square chimney required

to withstand force of wind [0 to 300,000])

where D = average width of side in feet (0 to 10); H = height of chimney in feet (0 to 100); F = force of wind = 50 for hurricane which is design condition; B = breadth of base in feet (0 to 15).

96. Time required for turning or boring work in the lathe is expressed by $T = L/FN$, where T = time in minutes for one cut over the work; L = length of cut in inches (6 to 72); N = rpm (10 to 1000); F = feed in inches per revolution (0.002 to 0.30).

97. Time required for planing and shaping is expressed by $T = W/FN$, where T = time in minutes; W = width of work in inches (3 to 60); F = feed per stroke in inches (0.01 to 0.25); N = number of cutting strokes per minute (2 to 75).

Electrical

98. $H = \dfrac{2\pi I r^2}{d^3}$ (field intensity at any point P as shown by the figure)

where I = current in wire in ab-amperes (0 to 500); r = in centimeters (1 to 10); d = in centimeters (1 to 20); H = in lines per square centimeter (0 to 50).

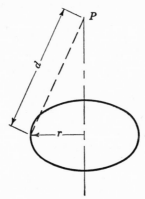

99. $R = \dfrac{\rho}{10^6} \dfrac{l}{D^2}$ (resistance of a wire in ohms [0 to 25])

where l = length of wire in feet (0 to 100); ρ = specific resistance (0 to 1000); D = diameter of the wire (0 to 0.1 in.).

100. $\dfrac{J}{V} = n_h B_{\max}{}^{1.6}$(ergs) (hysteresis loss per cubic centimeter per cycle in iron)

where n_h = constant varying from (0.001 to 0.004) for different types of iron; J = hysteresis loss in ergs (or convert to watts since one erg = 10^{-7} watt)

(0 to 50 watts); V = volume of iron in cubic centimeters (0 to 1000); B_{max} = maximum flux density (0 to 20,000).

101.
$$\cos \phi = \frac{P}{EI}$$

where ϕ is the phase angle in an alternating current circuit, ϕ varies (0° to 60°); P = power in watts as measured by a wattmeter (0 to 1000); E = voltage of circuit (0 to 250); I = current in amperes (0 to 20).

Aeronautical

102. $L = 0.00256 C_L A V^2$ (lift of an airfoil in pounds [1000 to 20,000]

where C_L = lift coefficient of airfoil section (0 to 2.0); A = area of airfoil, square feet (100 to 1000); V = velocity in miles per hour (50 to 300).

103. $F_{pr} = \dfrac{550n(\text{HP})}{V}$ (propeller thrust in pounds [100 to 1000])

where n = propeller efficiency in % varying from (65 to 90%); HP = engine horsepower (25 to 600); V = velocity of airplane in feet per second (50 to 400).

104. $V = 77.3 \left(n \dfrac{d}{P} \right)^{\frac{1}{3}}$ (airspeed at level in feet per second [50 to 400])

where n = propeller efficiency (65 to 90%); $d = W/A_D$, where W is the weight of the airplane and A_D is the equivalent drag area in square feet; d varies from (150 to 1000); $P = W/\text{HP}$, where HP is the horsepower of the engine, P varies from (1 to 15).

105. $R = \dfrac{(Kb)^2}{A}$ (aspect ratio of a wing, varies [4 to 8])

where K = Monk's span factor for biplanes, for monoplanes $K = 1.0$, varies from (1 to 1.5); b = span of longest wing in feet (20 to 80); A = total wing area in square feet (0 to 1500).

Chemical

106. $Q = 0.010386 \dfrac{a}{k} i$ (Faraday's law of electrolysis; $Q = \dfrac{m}{t}$ is the quantity deposited per second due to electrolysis and varies [0 to 10])

where a = the atomic weight (select a number of elements used in electrolysis); k = the valence of the element (1 to 4); i = electric current in amperes (1 to 10).

107. $W = \dfrac{144mP}{1544(t + 460)}$ (weight of a gas [0 to 6 lb per cu ft])

where P = pressure in pounds per square inch absolute (10 to 1000); m = molecular weight (2 to 200); t = temperature (0° to 600°F).

108. $W = VNM$ (titration equation where V milliliters of N normal
reagent are required to titrate W grams of a substance, the
the milliequivalent of which is M)

where V = milliliters (10 to 25); N = normal reagent (0.1 to 0.5); M = milliequivalent (0.02 to 0.20); W = grams of substance (0 to 2.5).

General

109. $C = \dfrac{WV^2}{gR}$ (centrifugal force acting on a body due to a rotation)

where W = weight in pounds of the body (1 to 150); V = velocity in feet per
second (1 to 50); R = the radius of the path in feet (0.1 to 10); $g = 32.2$;
C = centrifugal force in pounds (0 to 1500).

110. $\dfrac{u}{v} = \dfrac{20 + t_1}{20 + t_2}$

where u varies from 0 to 10; v varies from 0 to 10; t_1 varies from 0 to 100; t_2
varies from 0 to 100.

111. $(\Delta L) = L\,\alpha\,(t_2 - t_1)$, increase in length of a bar due to temperature changes

where L = length of bar (0 to 100 ft) and α = coefficient of expansion as given
by the following table:

Aluminum	= 0.0000244	Hardened steel	= 0.000010
Lead	= 0.000029	Copper	= 0.0000171
Wrought iron and mild steel	= 0.000011	Brass	= 0.0000198
Crown glass	= 0.000009	Tin	= 0.000027

$(t_2 - t_1)$, change in temperature in degrees Centigrade ($0°$ to $100°$)

112. $I = PRT$, (simple interest law)

where I = interest (0 to \$400); P = principal (\$1 to \$1000); R = rate of interest
per year period (4 to 8%); T = time or period in years (0 to 5 years) (subdivide
time scale into months).

113. $A = \tfrac{1}{2}bc \sin \alpha$ = area of a triangle shown in the figure

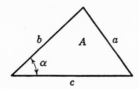

where $\alpha = (20°$ to $160°)$; $b = (0$ to 10$)$; $c = (0$ to 10$)$; $A = (0$ to 50$)$.

Chapter Nine

PROPORTIONAL CHARTS OF THE FORM

$$f_1(u) + f_2(v) = \frac{f_3(w)}{f_4(q)}$$

An equation of the above form can be solved by a combination of two types already discussed (Figure 64).

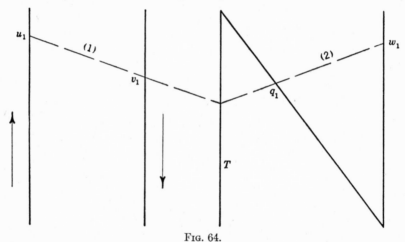

FIG. 64.

Let $$f_1(u) + f_2(v) = T \qquad (1) \qquad \text{(3 parallel scales)}$$

and $$T = \frac{f_3(w)}{f_4(q)} \qquad (2) \qquad \text{(Z chart)}$$

or $$f_3(w) = Tf_4(q)$$

Now let us consider another method for solving the above equation (Figure 65). Suppose that the parallel scales, A and B, are graduated in accordance with the scale equations:

$$X_u = m_u f_1(u)$$
$$X_v = m_v f_2(v)$$

and that the scale A also carries graduations for the $f_3(w)$, the scale equation of which is $X_w = m_w f_3(w)$. Let us further suppose that the

90

diagonal is graduated in accordance with the scale equation $X_q = m_q f_4(q)$.

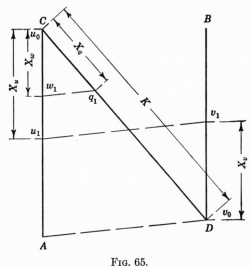

FIG. 65.

A study of Figure 65 reveals the following relation:

$$\frac{X_u + X_v}{K} = \frac{X_w}{X_q}$$

since triangles CAD and Cw_1q_1 are similar.

Or
$$\frac{m_u f_1(u) + m_v f_2(v)}{K} = \frac{m_w f_3(w)}{m_q f_4(q)}$$

If
$$f_1(u) + f_2(v) = \frac{f_3(w)}{f_4(q)}$$

then
$$m_v = m_u$$

and
$$\frac{m_u}{K} = \frac{m_w}{m_q}$$

or
$$m_q = \frac{K m_w}{m_u}$$

Hence, to construct an alignment chart of the above form:

(a) Graduate the left side of scale A from its scale equation, $X_u = m_u f_1(u)$.

(b) Graduate scale B from $X_v = m_u f_2(v)$.

(c) Graduate the right side of scale A from its scale equation, $X_w = m_w f_3(w)$.

(d) Graduate the diagonal scale from $X_q = m_q f_4(q)$, where $m_q = K m_w / m_u$.

Caution: Do not overlook the fact that point C is the zero value of functions u, w, and q; that point D is the zero value of function v.

EXAMPLE

$$V = \frac{\pi h}{9} \left(\frac{5}{4} D^2 + d^2 \right) \text{ (volume of a buoy) (Figure 66)}$$

where h = height of buoy (0 to 10 ft); D = diameter of midsection (0 to 10 ft); d = diameter of base (0 to 10 ft); and V = volume of buoy.

Then $\qquad \dfrac{5}{4} D^2 + d^2 = \dfrac{9V}{\pi h}$, which is of the form

$$f_1(u) + f_2(v) = \frac{f_3(w)}{f_4(q)}$$

$X_D = m_D \frac{5}{4} D^2 = 0.06 \frac{5}{4} D^2 = 0.075 D^2$ (scale length, 7.5 in.)

$X_d = m_d d^2 = 0.06 d^2$ (scale length, 6 in.)

$X_v = m_v 9V = 0.001 \times 9V = 0.009V$ (scale length approx. 7 in.)

$$\frac{m_V}{m_h} = \frac{m_D}{K}$$

or $\quad m_h = \dfrac{K m_v}{m_D} = \dfrac{0.001 \times K}{0.06} = \dfrac{0.1}{6} \dfrac{30}{\pi}$

$\qquad = \dfrac{0.5}{\pi}$, when $K = \dfrac{30}{\pi} = 9.55$ in.

$$X_h = m_h \pi h = \frac{0.5}{\pi} \pi h = 0.5h$$

Example: *Given*: $D = 8$; $d = 10$; $h = 5$. *Solution*: Join points 8 and 10 on the D and d scale, respectively. Through point 5 on the h scale draw a parallel line. This line cuts the V scale in point $V = 315$. By computation, $V = 314.29$.

Note: It should be recognized that the actual drawing of the parallel can be eliminated by scribing a family of parallels (so spread as to give desired accuracy in reading) on a transparent sheet. The prepared

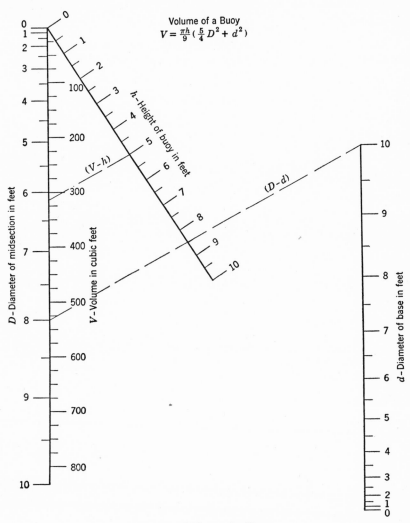

Fig. 66. Volume of a Buoy.

sheet could then be placed over the chart so that one of the parallels passes through 8 and 10 and another parallel * passes through point 5.

* In some cases it will be necessary to interpolate between two parallels.

If the equation is of the form $f_1(u) - f_2(v) = f_3(w)/f_4(q)$, positive values of u and v will be laid off in the same direction. This is shown in Figure 67.

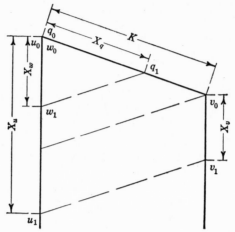

FIG. 67.

$$\frac{X_u - X_v}{K} = \frac{X_w}{X_q}$$

Again, if

$$X_u = m_u f_1(u)$$

$$X_v = m_u f_2(v)$$

$$X_w = m_w f_3(w)$$

$$X_q = m_q f_4(q)$$

and

$$\frac{m_u}{K} = \frac{m_w}{m_q}$$

Then

$$f_1(u) - f_2(v) = \frac{f_3(w)}{f_4(q)}$$

EXAMPLE

$$u^2 - v^2 = \frac{w}{4q} \quad \text{(Figure 68)}$$

u (0 to 5); v (0 to 5); q (0 to 6)

$X_u = m_u u^2 = 0.20u^2$ (for scale length of 5 in.)

$X_v = m_v v^2 = 0.20v^2$ (for scale length of 5 in.)

$X_w = m_w w = 0.01w$ (for scale length of 6 in.)

$$\frac{m_w}{m_q} = \frac{m_u}{K}$$

$$m_q = \frac{m_w}{m_u} K = \frac{0.01}{0.20} K = 0.05K = 0.05 \times 5 = 0.25, \text{ where } K = 5 \text{ in.}$$

$X_q = m_q 4q = 0.25 \times 4q = q$

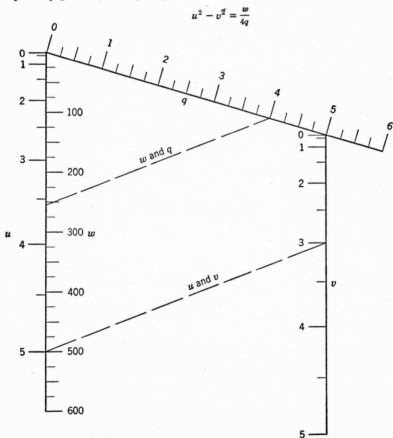

Fig. 68. Alignment Chart for the Equation, $u^2 - v^2 = \dfrac{w}{4q}$.

Example: *Given: u* = 5; *v* = 3; *q* = 4.

Required: w.

Solution. Join points 5 and 3 on the *u* and *v* scales, respectively. Through point 4 on the *q* scale, draw a line parallel to line 1 and read *w* = 255. By computation, *w* = 256.

If it is desired to construct a nomogram for an equation of the type form $f_1(u) + f_2(v) = f_3(w)/f_4(q)$ so that no double scales will be neces-

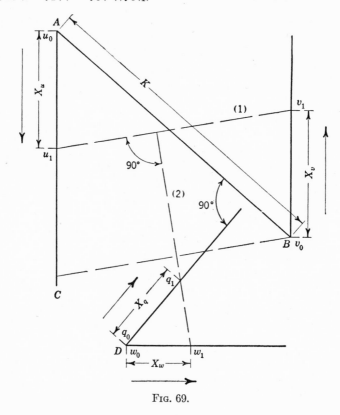

FIG. 69.

sary, another arrangement can be made which will overcome this situation.

Let us consider Figure 69. Scales *u* and *w* are at right angles. Similarly, scale *q* and the diagonal *AB*, which joins the zero values of functions *u* and *v*, are at right angles. Scales *u* and *v* are parallel.

The geometric relations can easily be determined by studying a typical case. Suppose line 1 joins any two points u_1 and v_1. Then let us draw line 2 through point w_1 and perpendicular to line 1. The intersection of line 2 with the q scale will give us point q_1, the desired solution. Why is this true?

In Figure 69 it will be seen that line BC is parallel to line 1. Again, triangles ABC and Dq_1w_1 are similar. Therefore

$$\frac{X_u + X_v}{K} = \frac{X_w}{X_q}$$

The remainder of the development is the same as shown previously.

There is an advantage in this design over the one which uses parallels, in that (1) there is a separate scale for each function and (2) the readings can be made by placing a transparent sheet, having but two lines at right angles, over the nomogram. Proper orientation of the lines can be made very quickly.

EXERCISES

114. $\quad A = \dfrac{d(b_1 + b_2)}{2}$ (area of a trapezoid)

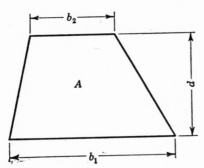

where $b_1 = $ (0 to 100); $b_2 = $ (0 to 80); $d = $ (0 to 50); $A = $ limits corresponding.

115. Weight of a hollow steel tube: $\quad W = \dfrac{\ell \pi (d^2 - d_1^2)}{4} \cdot \rho$

where $W = $ the weight (0 to 100 lb); $\ell = $ the length in inches (0 to 100); $d = $ the outside diameter (0 to 2 in.); $d_1 = $ the inside diameter (0 to 1.9 in.); $\rho = $ density $= 489.6/1728$ lb per cu in.

116. $\qquad KV = (p_1 + p_2)$

where V is the volume of earthwork per station; $p_1 + p_2$ are average planimeter readings in square inches from the cross section drawings, and K is a constant depending on the length of section and the scale: $V = $ (0 to 1000) in cubic yards, p_1 or p_2 (0 to 10), and $K = $ corresponding limits.

117. $F = \dfrac{k}{t^a}$ (Wall Thickness Sensitivity)

where F is the tensile strength of a metal or alloy, t is the thickness, k and "a" are constants depending on the kind of material.

$$F = (10 \text{ to } 50 \text{ kg per sq mm})$$

$$k = \text{constant } (10 \text{ to } 50 \text{ kg per sq mm})$$

$$t = (10 \text{ to } 90 \text{ mm})$$

$$a = (0.2 \text{ to } 0.7)$$

118. $R = (P - d)t55{,}000$ (strength of a riveted steel plate between rivet holes)

where P is the pitch of the rivets and d the diameter.

$$P = (0 \text{ to } 5 \text{ in.})$$

$$d = (0 \text{ to } 1 \text{ in.})$$

$$R = (0 \text{ to } 100{,}000 \text{ lb})$$

$$t = (0 \text{ to } 1 \text{ in.})$$

119. $\dfrac{T_d}{T_s} = e^{\mu\theta}$ (ratio of tensions in a rope used over a pulley as shown in the figure where T_d is the larger pull)

T_d varies (1 to 100 lb)

T_s varies (1 to 100 lb)

μ varies (0 to 0.4)

θ varies (0 to π)

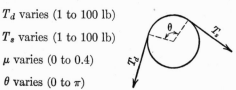

Chapter Ten

ALIGNMENT CHARTS FOR THE SOLUTION OF EQUATIONS OF THE FORM
$$f_1(u) + f_2(v) \cdot f_3(w) = f_4(w)$$

Suppose the parallel scales, A and B (Figure 70), are graduated in accordance with the scale equations:

$$X_u = m_u f_1(u)$$

$$X_v = m_v f_2(v)$$

It is further supposed that a straight line joining points u_1 and v_1 cuts the curved scale, C, in point w_1, which satisfies the equation.

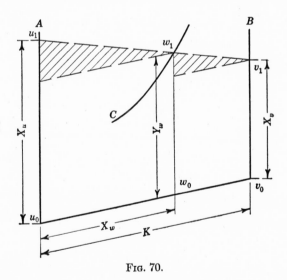

Fig. 70.

Points on the scale C are located by co-ordinates, X_w and Y_w. Let us develop expressions for X_w and Y_w.

99

From the similar triangles (shaded),

$$\frac{X_u - Y_w}{Y_w - X_v} = \frac{X_w}{K - X_w}$$

from which $\qquad X_u(K - X_w) + X_v X_w = KY_w$

or $\qquad X_u + X_v \left[\frac{X_w}{K - X_w}\right] = \left[\frac{KY_w}{K - X_w}\right]$

Now $\qquad m_u f_1(u) + m_v f_2(v) \left[\frac{X_w}{K - X_w}\right] = \left[\frac{KY_w}{K - X_w}\right]$

This is true since $X_u = m_u f_1(u)$ and $X_v = m_v f_2(v)$. Careful study of the above equation will show that $X_w/(K - X_w)$ must equal $Cf_3(w)$ and that the right-hand member, $KY_w/(K - X_w)$ must equal $C_1 f_4(w)$. In order to obtain the equation $f_1(u) + f_2(v) \cdot f_3(w) = f_4(w)$, it will be seen that $C = m_u/m_v$ and $C_1 = m_u$. This means that

$$\frac{X_w}{K - X_w} = \frac{m_u}{m_v} f_3(w) \quad \text{and} \quad \frac{KY_w}{K - X_w} = m_u f_4(w)$$

From $\qquad\qquad \dfrac{X_w}{K - X_w} = \dfrac{m_u}{m_v} f_3(w)$

$$X_w = \frac{K m_u f_3(w)}{m_u f_3(w) + m_v}$$

and from $\qquad\qquad \dfrac{KY_w}{K - X_w} = m_u f_4(w)$

$$Y_w = \frac{K m_u f_4(w) - X_w m_u f_4(w)}{K}$$

or $\qquad\qquad Y_w = m_u f_4(w) - \dfrac{m_u f_3(w) m_u f_4(w)}{m_u f_3(w) + m_v}$

$$Y_w = \frac{m_u m_v f_4(w)}{m_u f_3(w) + m_v}$$

Hence, to construct an alignment chart of the above form,
  (1) Graduate the A and B scales from their scale equations:

$$X_u = m_u f_1(u)$$
$$X_v = m_v f_2(v)$$

(2) Locate the curved scale by its co-ordinates:

$$X_w = \frac{K m_u f_3(w)}{m_u f_3(w) + m_v}$$

$$Y_w = \frac{m_u m_v f_4(w)}{m_u f_3(w) + m_v}$$

Caution. The axis from which distances Y_w are laid off is the line which joins the zero value of function, $f_1(u)$, with the zero value of function, $f_2(v)$.

EXAMPLE

$$w^2 + pw + q = 0 \text{ (quadratic formula)}$$

Transposing $\qquad q + pw = -w^2$

which is of the form

$$f_1(u) + f_2(v) \cdot f_3(w) = f_4(w)$$

$$X_q = m_q q = 0.6q$$

$$X_p = m_p p = 0.6p$$

where m_q and m_p were arbitrarily chosen as 0.6.

$$X_w = \frac{K m_u f_3(w)}{m_u f_3(w) + m_v}$$

If $\qquad K = 5 \text{ in.}$

$$X_w = \frac{5 \times 0.6 \times w}{0.6w + 0.6} = \frac{5w}{w + 1}$$

$$Y_w = \frac{m_u m_v f_4(w)}{m_u f_3(w) + m_v}$$

$$= \frac{0.6 \times 0.6(-w^2)}{0.6w + 0.6} = \frac{-0.6w^2}{w + 1}$$

See Figure 71 for graphical solution.

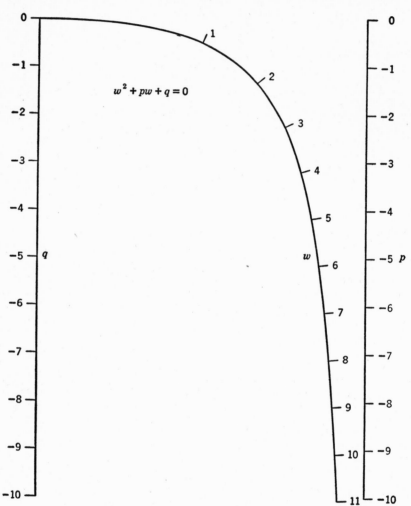

$w^2 + pw + q = 0$

Fɪɢ. 71. Alignment Chart for the Equation, $w^2 + pw + q = 0$.

EXERCISES

120. $Q = 3.33(B - 0.2H)H^{3/2}$ (Francis formula for the quantity of water flowing over a contracted weir)

where B = width of the weir in feet (0 to 5); H = head over the crest (0 to 5 ft); Q = calculate limits.

121. $S = V_0 t - \frac{1}{2}gt^2$ (distance traveled by a body projected upward with a velocity v_o, after a time, t)

where S = distance in feet (calculate limits); v_o = velocity in feet per second (0 to 100); t = time in seconds (0 to 5); and g = 32.2.

122. $\left(\dfrac{I}{y}\right) = 0.0982 \left(\dfrac{D^4 - d^4}{D}\right)$ (section modulus of a hollow tube whose inside and outside diameters are D and d, respectively)

where D varies (0 to 10 in.) and d varies (0 to 9 in.).

123. $V = 0.649 \dfrac{T}{p} - \dfrac{22.58}{p^{3/4}}$ (specific volume in cubic feet of super-heated steam under a pressure of p pounds per square inch and with a temperature, T, in degrees Fahrenheit)

where T varies (220 to 600); p = (30 to 200).

124. $V = \frac{1}{2}\pi r^2 h + \frac{1}{6}\pi h^3$ (volume of a spherical segment with one base)

where h is the altitude of the segment and r the radius of the sphere. r varies (0 to 10 in.) and h varies (0 to 10 in.).

Chapter Eleven

MISCELLANEOUS FORMS

1. $\dfrac{f_1(u) + f_2(v)}{f_1(u) - f_2(v)} = \dfrac{f_3(w)}{f_4(q)}$ (Figure 72)

$$X_u = m_u f_1(u) \qquad\qquad X_w = m_w f_3(w)$$

$$X_v = m_v f_2(v) \qquad\qquad X_q = m_q f_4(q)$$

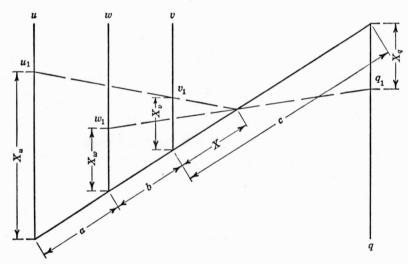

Fig. 72. Chart for an Equation of the Form, $\dfrac{f_1(u) + f_2(v)}{f_1(u) - f_2(v)} = \dfrac{f_3(w)}{f_4(q)}$.

From similar triangles,

$$\frac{X_u}{X_v} = \frac{a + b + X}{X}$$

$$\frac{X_w}{X_q} = \frac{b + X}{c - X}$$

104

Eliminating X,

$$\frac{X_w}{X_q} = \frac{b + \dfrac{a + b}{\dfrac{X_u}{X_v} - 1}}{c - \dfrac{a + b}{\dfrac{X_u}{X_v} - 1}}$$

and simplifying,

$$\frac{X_w}{X_q} = \frac{bX_u + aX_v}{cX_u - (a + b + c)X_v}$$

then

$$\frac{m_w f_3(w)}{m_q f_4(q)} = \frac{bm_u f_1(u) + am_v f_2(v)}{cm_u f_1(u) - (a + b + c)m_v f_2(v)}$$

If

$$b = \frac{m_v}{m_u} \cdot a, \quad a + b + c = c\frac{m_u}{m_v}$$

and

$$\frac{m_w}{m_q} = \frac{am_v}{cm_u}$$

it can be shown that

$$\frac{f_1(u) + f_2(v)}{f_1(u) - f_2(v)} = \frac{f_3(w)}{f_4(q)}$$

By algebraic manipulation of the three previous substitutions,

$$\frac{m_u + m_v}{m_u - m_v} = \frac{m_q}{m_w}$$

$$\frac{a}{b} = \frac{m_u}{m_v}$$

$$\frac{a + b + c}{c} = \frac{m_u}{m_v} \quad \text{(Intermediate steps are left}$$
$$\text{to the reader)}$$

2. The type form discussed above can be represented by an alignment chart of the design shown in Figure 73. The scales for $f_1(u)$ and $f_2(u)$ are at right angles; likewise, the scales for $f_3(w)$ and $f_4(q)$ are at right angles; and a 45° angle exists between the $f_1(u)$ and $f_3(w)$ scales. If values u_1, v_1, and w_1 are selected, the value of q_1 is obtained by drawing a line through w_1, parallel to the line joining u_1 with v_1.

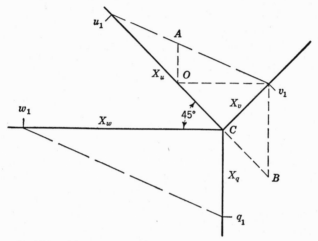

FIG. 73. Alternate Form of Chart for the Equation in Fig. 72.

Let us examine the geometry of the figure. Triangles u_1v_1B and u_1AO are similar (from the construction shown). Therefore,

$$\frac{u_1C + CB}{u_1O} = \frac{v_1B}{AO}$$

or

$$\frac{X_u + X_v}{X_u - X_v} = \frac{v_1B}{AO}$$

Also, triangles AOv_1 and w_1Cq_1 are similar. Hence,

$$\frac{Ov_1}{AO} = \frac{X_w}{X_q}$$

Since

$$Ov_1 = v_1B$$

$$\frac{X_u + X_v}{X_u - X_v} = \frac{X_w}{X_q}$$

If
$$X_u = m_u f_1(u)$$
$$X_v = m_v f_2(v)$$
$$X_w = m_w f_3(w)$$
$$X_q = m_q f_4(q)$$

then
$$\frac{m_u f_1(u) + m_v f_2(v)}{m_u f_1(u) - m_v f_2(v)} = \frac{m_w f_3(w)}{m_q f_4(q)}$$

This means that $m_u = m_v$ and $m_w = m_q$ if

$$\frac{f_1(u) + f_2(v)}{f_1(u) - f_2(v)} = \frac{f_3(w)}{f_4(q)}$$

3. $f_1(u)\cdot f_2(v) + f_3(w)\cdot f_4(q) = f_5(q)$

Let
$$f_1(u)\cdot f_2(v) = T \qquad (1)$$

and
$$T + f_3(w)\cdot f_4(q) = f_5(q) \qquad (2)$$

Thus a combination of a Z chart and one involving two straight lines and a curve can be formed to solve the above equation (Figure 74).

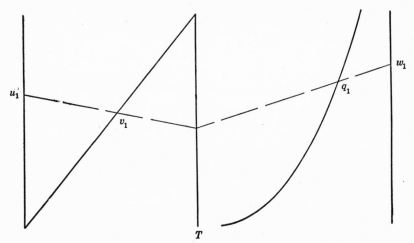

FIG. 74. Alignment Chart for an Equation of the Form, $f_1(u)\cdot f_2(v) + f_3(w)\cdot f_4(q) = f_5(q)$.

4. $f_1(u) + f_2(v) \cdot f_3(w) = f_4(q)$ (Figure 75)

Let $$f_2(v) \cdot f_3(w) = T$$

and $$f_1(u) + T = f_4(q)$$

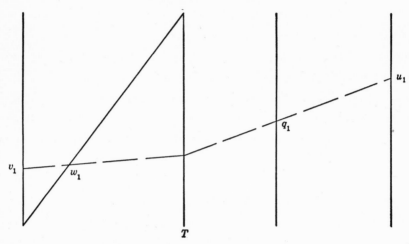

FIG. 75. Alignment Chart for an Equation of the Form, $f_1(u) + f_2(v) \cdot f_3(w) = f_4(q)$.

5. $\dfrac{1}{f_1(u)} + \dfrac{f_4(w)}{f_2(v)} = \dfrac{1}{f_3(w)}$ (Figure 76)

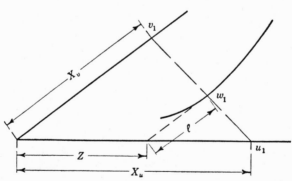

FIG. 76. Alignment Chart for an Equation. of the Form, $\dfrac{1}{f_1(u)} + \dfrac{f_4(w)}{f_2(v)} = \dfrac{1}{f_3(w)}$.

$$X_u = m_u f_1(u) \qquad\qquad Z = m_u f_3(w)$$

$$X_v = m_v f_2(v) \qquad\qquad L = m_v f_3(w) f_4(w)$$

Points on the curve are located from

$$Z = m_u f_3(w)$$

and

$$l = m_v f_3(w) f_4(w)$$

in the following manner:

1. Graduate a *temporary* w scale along the horizontal scale for $f_1(u)$.
2. Draw lines through points on the temporary w scale, parallel to the v scale.
3. On these lines lay off distances obtained from $l = m_v f_3(w) f_4(w)$, using the same value of w through which the parallels were drawn.

6. $f_1(u) \cdot f_2(v) \cdot f_3(w) = f_4(q) \cdot f_5(r)$ (Figure 77)

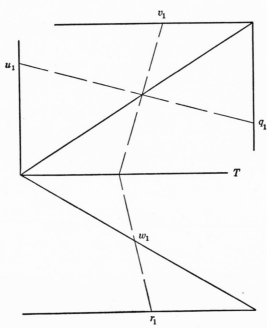

FIG. 77. Combination Proportional and Z Chart for an Equation of the Form, $f_1(u) \cdot f_2(v) \cdot f_3(w) = f_4(q) \cdot f_5(r)$.

Let

$$\frac{f_1(u)}{f_4(q)} = \frac{T}{f_2(v)} \qquad \text{(proportional chart) (1)}$$

and
$$\frac{f_5(r)}{T} = \frac{f_3(w)}{1} \tag{2}$$

or
$$f_5(r) = Qf_3(w) \qquad \text{(Z chart)}$$

Note: An alternate form could be developed by expressing the given equation logarithmically, resulting in an alignment chart having parallel scales.

7. $f_1(u) \cdot f_2(v) \cdot f_3(w) = f_4(q) \cdot f_5(r) \cdot f_6(s)$ (Figure 78)

Let
$$\frac{f_1(u)}{f_4(q)} = \frac{T}{f_2(v)} \tag{1}$$

$$\frac{f_5(r)}{T} = \frac{f_3(w)}{f_6(s)} \tag{2}$$

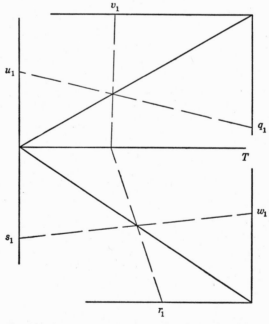

FIG. 78. Combination Proportional Charts for an Equation of the Form,
$$f_1(u) \cdot f_2(v) \cdot f_3(w) = f_4(q) \cdot f_5(r) \cdot f_6(s).$$

8. DESIGN OF NET CHARTS

Problems involving four variables may also be solved by a net chart which makes it possible to read all four variables with one isopleth. The principles involved in the design of this type chart are the same as those employed in the design of a chart of the form, $f_1(u) + f_2(v) = f_3(w)$.

EXAMPLE

Suppose the given equation is $S = V_0 t + \frac{1}{2}at^2$, where $S =$ distance traversed in feet (0 to 15), $V_0 =$ initial velocity in feet per second (0 to 10), $a =$ acceleration in feet per second^2 (0 to 4), and $t =$ time interval in seconds (1 to 4).

Solution. Let $t = 1, 2, 3,$ and 4. With these values for t, the following equations result, namely:

$$S = V_0 + \frac{a}{2} \tag{1}$$

$$S = 2V_0 + 2a \tag{2}$$

$$S = 3V_0 + \tfrac{9}{2}a \tag{3}$$

$$S = 4V_0 + 8a \tag{4}$$

All the above equations are of the form $f_1(u) + f_2(v) = f_3(w)$.

Consider the first equation, $S = V_0 + a/2$. It may be written $V_0 - S = -a/2$ to conform with the type equation $f_1(u) + f_2(v) = f_3(w)$. Suppose that the desired length of the V_0 and S scales is 10 units; then, the scale equations are:

$$X_{v_0} = V_0 \quad \text{and} \quad X_s = \tfrac{2}{3}S.$$

From the above moduli, the modulus for the a scale is $\dfrac{1 \times \frac{2}{3}}{1 + \frac{2}{3}} = \dfrac{2}{5}$; and

its position is determined from the ratio $\dfrac{1}{\frac{2}{3}} = \dfrac{3}{2}$. The scale equation

for a then becomes $X_a = \tfrac{2}{5}(a/2) = a/5$. The chart for the equation $V_0 - S = -a/2$ is shown in Figure 79.

Now, consider equation 2, $S = 2V_0 + 2a$. This equation can be rewritten in type form as $2V_0 - S = -2a$.

If we are to use the same V_0 and S scales as shown in Figure 79, the effective moduli for the scale equations, $X_{v_0} = m_{v_0}(2V_0)$ and $X_s = m_s S$, must be the same as those used in equation 1.

This means that m_{v_0} must equal $\tfrac{1}{2}$ in order for the effective modulus to equal one. Therefore, the scale equation for V_0 in equation 2 is $X_{v_0} = \frac{1}{2}(2V_0) = V_0$.

Since the coefficient of S is the same in both equations 1 and 2, no change in modulus for the S scale is necessary. Note, however, that the location of the a scale is determined by the ratio $\dfrac{m_{v_0}}{m_s} = \dfrac{\frac{1}{2}}{\frac{2}{3}} = \dfrac{3}{4}$.

The chart for equation 2 is shown in Figure 80.

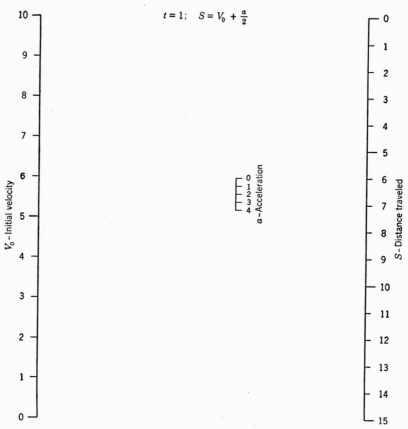

Fig. 79.   First Step in Designing a Net Chart for the Equation, $S = V_0 t + \frac{1}{2}at^2$.

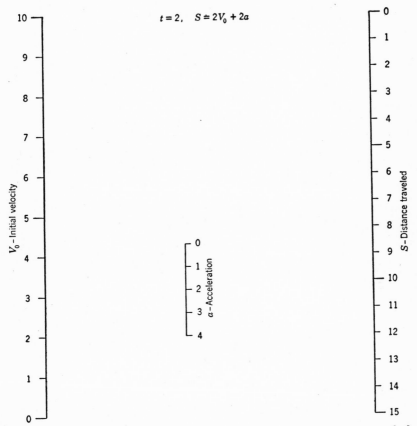

FIG. 80. Second Step in Designing a Net Chart for the Equation, $S = V_0 t + \frac{1}{2} a t^2$.

If the two charts are superposed, the resulting chart, Figure 81, would be obtained.

It should be clear that similar calculations for equations 3 and 4 would be necessary to complete the net chart. It is not necessary to

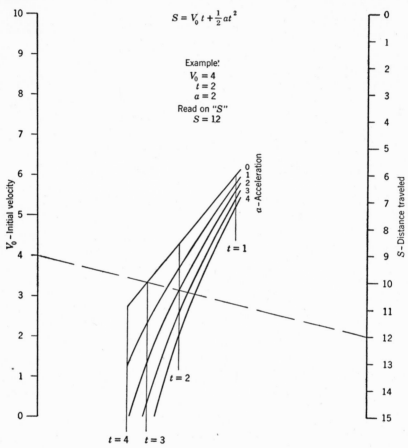

FIG. 81.   Net Chart for the Equation, $S = V_0 t + \frac{1}{2}at^2$.

make separate charts for each of the four equations, since the V_0 and S scales are the same in all cases. Calculations for positioning the a scale are necessary and, in addition, the moduli for the a scales must be computed in order to graduate these scales properly. Finally, curves drawn through like values of a will establish the net for the variable a. The net for the variable, t, consists of the vertical lines which first carried the values of a when t equaled 1, 2, 3, and 4. The completed chart is shown in Figure 81.

EXERCISES

125.
$$f = \frac{9Wl}{bd^2}$$

when f = fiber stress (500 to 2500 psi); l = length of wooden beam (5 to 30 ft); W = total load (1000 to 12,000 lb); b = width of beam (2 to 12 in.); d = depth of beam (4 to 16 in.).

126.
$$\Delta_{max} = \frac{Pl^3}{48EI}$$

where Δ = deflection of a simple beam with a concentrated load at the center, in inches; P = concentrated load (500 to 10,000 lb); l = length of beam (60 to 300 in.); E = modulus of elasticity (2×10^6 to 30×10^6 psi); I = moment of inertia (1000 to 20,000 in.^{4}).

127.
$$\Delta_{max} = \frac{Wl^3}{KEI}$$

where Δ is deflection in inches of simple beams loaded as follows: (*a*) uniformly ($K = 384/5$), (*b*) load increasing uniformly to one end ($K = 1000/13$), (*c*) load increasing uniformly to the center ($K = 60$); W = total load (10,000 to 300,000 lb); E and I as above; and l = (120 to 600 in.).

SUMMARY OF TYPE FORMS

1. $$f_1(u) + f_2(v) = f_3(w)$$

Scale equations:

$$X_u = m_u f_1(u)$$

$$X_v = m_v f_2(v)$$

$$X_w = \frac{m_u m_v}{m_u + m_v} f_3(w)$$

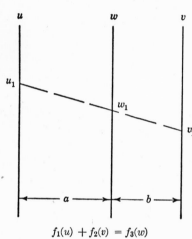

Scale location:

$$\frac{a}{b} = \frac{m_u}{m_v}$$

$$f_1(u) + f_2(v) = f_3(w)$$

2. $$f_1(u) = f_2(v) \cdot f_3(w)$$

Scale equations:

$$X_u = m_u f_1(u)$$

$$X_v = m_v f_2(v)$$

$$X_w = \frac{K}{K_1 f_3(w) + 1}$$

where $K_1 = \dfrac{m_u}{m_v}$ and K is the length of the diagonal.

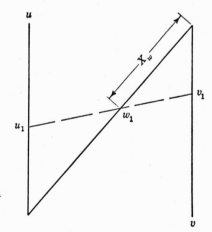

$$f_1(u) = f_2(v) \cdot f_3(w)$$

3.
$$f_1(u) + f_2(v) = \frac{f_1(u)}{f_3(w)}$$

Scale equations:

$$X_u = m_u f_1(u)$$

$$X_v = m_v f_2(v)$$

$$m_u = m_v$$

$$X_w = K f_3(w)$$

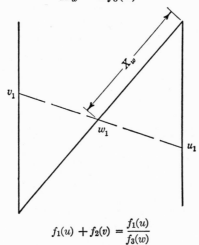

$$f_1(u) + f_2(v) = \frac{f_1(u)}{f_3(w)}$$

4.
$$\frac{1}{f_1(u)} + \frac{1}{f_2(v)} = \frac{1}{f_3(w)}$$

Scale equations:

$$X_u = m_u f_1(u)$$

$$X_v = m_v f_2(v)$$

Location of w scale:

$$\frac{Z}{l} = \frac{m_v}{m_u}$$

Graduate w scale by

(a) $Z = m_v f_3(w)$ and parallels to u scale,

or   (b) $X_w = [m_v{}^2 + m_u{}^2 + 2m_u m_v \cos \theta]^{\frac{1}{2}} \cdot f_3(w)$

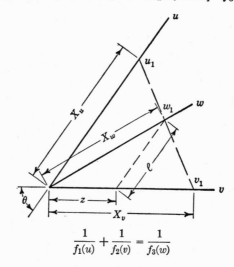

$$\frac{1}{f_1(u)} + \frac{1}{f_2(v)} = \frac{1}{f_3(w)}$$

5. $$f_1(u) + f_2(v) + f_3(w) \cdots = f_4(q)$$

See Type 1.

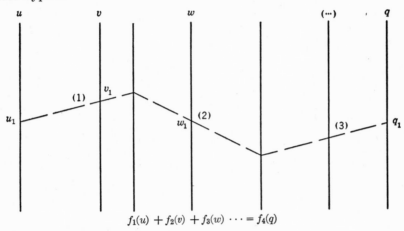

$$f_1(u) + f_2(v) + f_3(w) \cdots = f_4(q)$$

6. $$\frac{f_1(u)}{f_2(v)} = \frac{f_3(w)}{f_4(q)}$$

Scale equations:

$$X_u = m_u f_1(u) \qquad\qquad X_w = m_w f_3(w)$$

$$X_v = m_v f_2(v) \qquad\qquad X_q = m_q f_4(q)$$

and

$$\frac{m_u}{m_v} = \frac{m_w}{m_q}$$

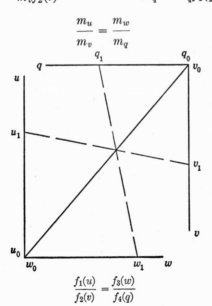

$$\frac{f_1(u)}{f_2(v)} = \frac{f_3(w)}{f_4(q)}$$

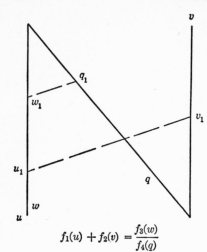

7. $f_1(u) + f_2(v) = \dfrac{f_3(w)}{f_4(q)}$

Scale equations:

$$X_u = m_u f_1(u)$$

$$X_v = m_v f_2(v)$$

$$X_w = m_w f_3(w)$$

$$m_u = m_v$$

$$X_q = m_q f_4(q) \text{ where } m_q = \dfrac{K m_w}{m_u}$$

$$f_1(u) + f_2(v) = \dfrac{f_3(w)}{f_4(q)}$$

8. $$f_1(u) + f_2(v) = \dfrac{f_3(w)}{f_4(q)}$$

Same as in 7.   Alternate form of chart shown below.

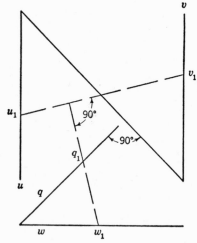

Alternate Form for $f_1(u) + f_2(v) = \dfrac{f_3(w)}{f_4(q)}$

9. $$f_1(u) + f_2(v)f_3(w) = f_4(w)$$

Scale equations:

$$X_u = m_u f_1(u)$$

$$X_v = m_v f_2(v)$$

$$X_w = \frac{K m_u f_3(w)}{m_u f_3(w) + m_v}$$

$$Y_w = \frac{m_u m_v f_4(w)}{m_u f_3(w) + m_v}$$

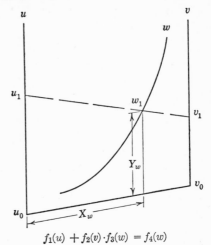

$$f_1(u) + f_2(v) \cdot f_3(w) = f_4(w)$$

Chapter Twelve

PRACTICAL SHORT-CUTS IN THE DESIGN OF ALIGNMENT CHARTS

If the designer is thoroughly grounded in the theory of alignment charts and fully understands the mathematical methods employed in changing a given equation to a type form, it is frequently possible to short-cut the actual construction of the chart.

EXAMPLE 1

Suppose that the given equation is $M = wl^2/8$ (bending moment in foot-pounds), where the ranges are w (10 to 300 lb per ft) and l (5 to 30 ft).

If a chart consisting of parallel scales is desired, the designer recognizes the fact that the equation can be converted to the form:

$$\log w + 2 \log l = \log M + \log 8$$

The chart can now be constructed without making any further calculations. The following procedure is suggested:

1. Draw two parallel lines any convenient distance apart.
2. Graduate the left-hand scale for w by simply marking the lower point 10 and the upper point 300. Other points on the scale may be located by projecting from a log scale (two-deck slide rule scale or commercial log sheets having two decks).
3. Mark the lower point of the l scale 5 and the upper point 30. Again, locate additional graduations by projecting from a log scale.
4. Now calculate two points for M, i.e.:
(a) Let $w = 40$ and $l = 10$. This yields $M = 500$.
(b) Let $w = 160$ and $l = 5$. This yields $M = 500$.

The point in which the line joining 40 and 10 intersects the line joining 160 and 5 is point $M = 500$. The vertical line through this point locates the M scale. A second point on this scale can be now located

122

by letting $w = 40$ and $l = 30$, which yield $M = 4500$. The line joining $w = 40$ with $l = 30$, then cuts the M scale in point 4500. Other points may be obtained by projecting from a log scale. The completed chart is shown in Figure 82.

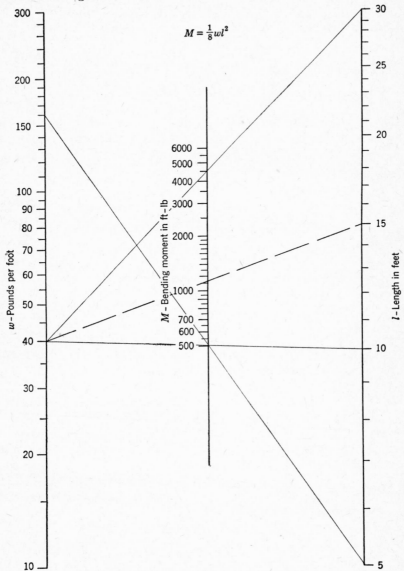

Fig. 82. Alignment Chart for the Equation, $M = \frac{1}{8}wl^2$, Constructed by the Short-Cut Method.

EXAMPLE 2

Consider the equation,

$$S = 0.0982 \left(\frac{D^4 - d^4}{D} \right) \text{ (section modulus for tubes and bars)}$$

where D and d = (0 to 10 in.) and S = (0 to 100 in.^{3}).

The equation may be converted to the form, $0.0982d^4 + DS = 0.0982D^4$, which is in the type form, $f_1(u) + f_2(v) \cdot f_3(w) = f_4(w)$.

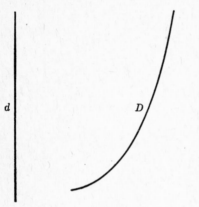

FIG. 83.

The chart will consist of two parallel scales for d and S respectively, and a curved scale for D. A preliminary sketch of the chart would look something like Figure 83.

The following procedure is suggested:

1. Draw the d and S scales a convenient distance apart.

2. Mark the lower point on the d scale, 0 and the upper point 10.

3. Likewise, mark the lower and upper points on the S scale 0 and 100, respectively. Since the function of S is linear, this scale will be uniform and can be readily graduated.

4. The d scale can be graduated by first laying out a d^4 scale and then projecting this scale to the d scale.

5. If $S = 0$, then $d^4 = D^4$. Draw lines through $S = 0$ and points on the d scale. Somewhere on these lines will be found the corresponding values of D.

6. Now let $d = 0$; then $DS = 0.0982D^4$. From this equation, we can determine values of S for given values of D.

D	5	6	7	8	9	10
S	12.3	21.2	33.7	50.3	71.6	98.2

Now draw lines through $d = 0$, and the values of S shown in the table above.

7. Obtain the points of intersection of those lines having a common value of D. The curve joining these points constitutes the D scale. (See Figure 84.)

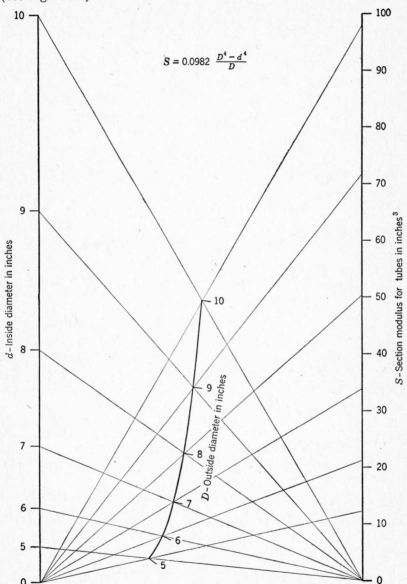

$$S = 0.0982 \frac{D^4 - d^4}{D}$$

FIG. 84. Alignment Chart for the Equation, $S = 0.0982 \dfrac{D^4 - d^4}{D}$, Constructed by the Short-Cut Method.

Chapter Thirteen

THE USE OF DETERMINANTS IN THE DESIGN AND CONSTRUCTION OF ALIGNMENT CHARTS

Most students find the geometric method discussed in the previous chapters a simple and direct approach to the design and construction of alignment charts. It is felt, however, that an introduction to the method which employs determinants is desirable so that students will be enabled

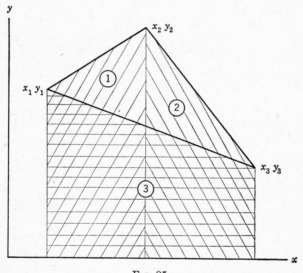

Fig. 85.

to comprehend, more fully, treatments based on determinants exclusively.

Let us consider Figure 85. The area of the triangle may be obtained by the difference between the area of trapezoid 3 and the sum of the areas of trapezoids 1 and 2; or

Area of triangle

$$= \tfrac{1}{2}[(y_2 + y_1)(x_2 - x_1) + (y_2 + y_3)(x_3 - x_2) - (y_1 + y_3)(x_3 - x_1)]$$

126

In determinant form this would be

$$A = \tfrac{1}{2} \begin{vmatrix} x_1 & y_1 & 1 \\ x_2 & y_2 & 1 \\ x_3 & y_3 & 1 \end{vmatrix}$$

If point $x_2 y_2$ were placed on the line joining $x_1 y_1$ with $x_3 y_3$, the points are said to be co-linear, or the area of the triangle is zero. Hence

$$A = \tfrac{1}{2} \begin{vmatrix} x_1 & y_1 & 1 \\ x_2 & y_2 & 1 \\ x_3 & y_3 & 1 \end{vmatrix} = 0$$

or when

$$\begin{vmatrix} x_1 & y_1 & 1 \\ x_2 & y_2 & 1 \\ x_3 & y_3 & 1 \end{vmatrix} = 0$$

the points $x_1 y_1$, $x_2 y_2$, and $x_3 y_3$ are on the same line.

EXAMPLE 1

Suppose we have the determinant

$$\begin{vmatrix} 0 & u & 1 \\ 1 & v & 1 \\ \tfrac{1}{2} & \dfrac{w}{2} & 1 \end{vmatrix} = 0$$

1. What does the determinant mean?
2. How can we construct an alignment chart from this determinant?
   In order to answer the first question, we must learn how to expand, or evaluate, the determinant, which is done in the following manner:

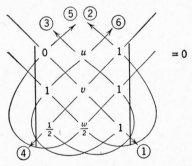

(*a*) Multiply 0, v, and 1. This is step 1 (see arrow).
(*b*) Multiply 1, $w/2$, and 1. This is step 2 (see arrow).

(c) Multiply $\frac{1}{2}$, 1, and u. This is step 3 (see arrow).

(d) Add the results of steps (a), (b), and (c). Thus far we have:

$$\left[0 + \frac{w}{2} + \frac{u}{2} \right]$$

Now start in the upper right-hand corner.

(e) Multiply 1, v, and $\frac{1}{2}$. This is step 4 (see arrow).

(f) Multiply 1, $w/2$, and 0. This is step 5 (see arrow).

(g) Multiply 1, 1, and u. This is step 6 (see arrow).

(h) Add the results of steps e, f, and g. This is

$$\left[\frac{v}{2} + 0 + u \right]$$

Finally, subtract h from d, i.e.,

$$\frac{w}{2} + \frac{u}{2} - \frac{v}{2} - u = 0$$

or
$$u + v - w = 0$$

Now with regard to the second question. If we consider $0, u$ as $x_1 y_1$; $1, v$ as $x_2 y_2$; and $\frac{1}{2}, w/2$ as $x_3 y_3$, we may plot points for u, v, and w by assigning definite values such as $0, 1, 2, 3 \cdots n$ to each.

Since the x value is zero for all values of u, all points of u will lie on the Y axis. Likewise, since $x_2 = 1$, all points of v will lie on a line parallel to the Y axis and one unit to the right. Similarly, $x_3 = \frac{1}{2}$, and all points of w will lie on a line parallel to the Y axis and a $\frac{1}{2}$ unit to the right. It should be observed that since $y_3 = w/2$, the distance between consecutive values of w will be half the distance between consecutive values of u or v.

A straight line which joins a point on the u scale with one on the v scale will cut the w scale in a value which satisfies the equation $u + v = w$ (Figure 86). While the above material is easy to follow, one may wonder how the determinant

$$\begin{vmatrix} 0 & u & 1 \\ 1 & v & 1 \\ \frac{1}{2} & \frac{w}{2} & 1 \end{vmatrix} = 0$$

was developed in the first place. This could have been done by trial and error, observing that the right-hand column must consist of ones, and that only one variable should appear in each row.

A better approach, one which is direct and mathematically correct, is this:

(*a*) First, write the equation $u + v - w = 0$.

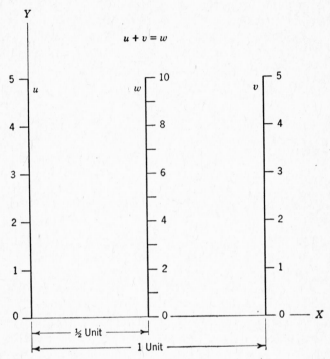

Fig. 86.   Chart for the Equation, $u + v = w$, Constructed by the Method of Determinants.

(*b*) Second, let $x = u$, and $y = v$.

(*c*) Third, write the expressions

$$x - u = 0$$

$$y - v = 0$$

$$x + y - w = 0$$

It should be noted that we now have three equations in x and y. If they are consistent, the determinant made up from the coefficients of

x and y and the constant term must vanish. [See Bocher's text *Introduction to Higher Algebra* (Chapter Four).] This means that

$$\begin{vmatrix} 1 & 0 & -u \\ 0 & 1 & -v \\ 1 & 1 & -w \end{vmatrix} = 0$$

The value of this determinant is $u + v = w$. You will recall that the determinant must be in the form

$$\begin{vmatrix} x_1 & y_1 & 1 \\ x_2 & y_2 & 1 \\ x_3 & y_3 & 1 \end{vmatrix} = 0$$

before the chart can be constructed. How can we manipulate the determinant in order to transform it to the form,

$$\begin{vmatrix} 0 & u & 1 \\ 1 & v & 1 \\ \frac{1}{2} & \frac{w}{2} & 1 \end{vmatrix} = 0$$

Let us start with

$$\begin{vmatrix} 1 & 0 & -u \\ 0 & 1 & -v \\ 1 & 1 & -w \end{vmatrix} = 0$$

Column 1 may be replaced by the sum of columns 1 and 2, yielding

$$\begin{vmatrix} 1 & 0 & u \\ 1 & 1 & v \\ 2 & 1 & w \end{vmatrix} = 0 \quad \text{(Note column 3 above was multiplied by } -1.)$$

Now the bottom row may be divided by 2, resulting in

$$\begin{vmatrix} 1 & 0 & u \\ 1 & 1 & v \\ 1 & \frac{1}{2} & \frac{w}{2} \end{vmatrix} = 0$$

By interchanging columns we get,

$$\begin{vmatrix} 0 & u & 1 \\ 1 & v & 1 \\ \frac{1}{2} & \dfrac{w}{2} & 1 \end{vmatrix} = 0$$

which is known as the "design determinant." All the steps shown above are permissible when the value of the determinant is zero. Rules for operating determinants are available in any good algebra textbook.

EXAMPLE 2

Given: $u + vw = w^2$
Required: The design determinant.
Solution: Let $x = u$ and $y = v$.

Now

$$x - u = 0 \tag{1}$$

$$y - v = 0 \tag{2}$$

$$x + yw - w^2 = 0 \tag{3}$$

If these equations are consistent, then

$$\begin{vmatrix} 1 & 0 & -u \\ 0 & 1 & -v \\ 1 & w & -w^2 \end{vmatrix} = 0$$

Replace column one by the sum of the first two columns.

$$\begin{vmatrix} 1 & 0 & u \\ 1 & 1 & v \\ w+1 & w & w^2 \end{vmatrix} = 0$$

Divide the bottom row by $w + 1$.

$$\begin{vmatrix} 1 & 0 & u \\ 1 & 1 & v \\ 1 & \dfrac{w}{w+1} & \dfrac{w^2}{w+1} \end{vmatrix} = 0$$

Rearrange the columns.

$$\begin{vmatrix} 0 & u & 1 \\ 1 & v & 1 \\ \dfrac{w}{w+1} & \dfrac{w^2}{w+1} & 1 \end{vmatrix} = 0$$

Construct the chart from the above determinant (Figure 87).

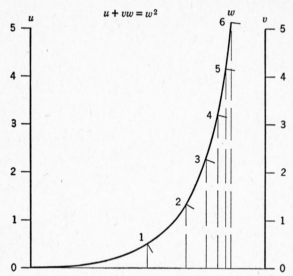

FIG. 87.   Chart for the Equation, $u + vw = w^2$, Constructed by the Method of Determinants.

Points on the w scale can be plotted from the following co-ordinates:

w	0	1	2	3	4	5
x-co-ordinate: $\dfrac{w}{w+1}$	0	$\frac{1}{2}$	$\frac{2}{3}$	$\frac{3}{4}$	$\frac{4}{5}$	$\frac{5}{6}$
y-co-ordinate: $\dfrac{w^2}{w+1}$	0	$\frac{1}{2}$	$\frac{4}{3}$	$\frac{9}{4}$	$\frac{16}{5}$	$\frac{25}{6}$

Up to this point no mention has been made of scale moduli.   In practical alignment charts this is a significant consideration.

EXAMPLE 3

Suppose we consider the equation $u + v = w$ again. Let us assume that u varies from 2 to 10 and that v varies from 5 to 15. You will recall that we had written the expressions,

$$x - u = 0$$

$$y - v = 0$$

$$x + y - w = 0$$

Now, however, let us introduce the scale moduli by writing

$$x - m_u u = 0$$

$$y - m_v v = 0$$

and
$$\frac{x}{m_u} + \frac{y}{m_v} - w = 0 \text{ (since } u + v - w = 0)$$

We can write the determinant,

$$\begin{vmatrix} 1 & 0 & -m_u u \\ 0 & 1 & -m_v v \\ \dfrac{1}{m_u} & \dfrac{1}{m_v} & -w \end{vmatrix} = 0$$

because the three equations above are consistent. This determinant may be reduced to the "design determinant" in the following manner:

$$\begin{vmatrix} 1 & 0 & m_u u \\ 0 & 1 & m_v v \\ \dfrac{1}{m_u} & \dfrac{1}{m_v} & w \end{vmatrix} = \begin{vmatrix} 1 & 0 & m_u u \\ 1 & 1 & m_v v \\ \dfrac{m_u + m_v}{m_u m_v} & \dfrac{1}{m_v} & w \end{vmatrix} = \begin{vmatrix} 1 & 0 & m_u u \\ 1 & 1 & m_v v \\ 1 \dfrac{m_u}{m_u + m_v} & \dfrac{m_u m_v}{m_u + m_v} & w \end{vmatrix} =$$

$$\begin{vmatrix} 0 & m_u u & 1 \\ 1 & m_v v & 1 \\ \dfrac{m_u}{m_u + m_v} & \dfrac{m_u m_v}{m_u + m_v} & w & 1 \end{vmatrix} = 0 \quad \leftarrow \text{Design Determinant}$$

If the lengths of the u and v scales are 6 in., then

$$m_u = \frac{6}{10 - 2} = \frac{3}{4}$$

and
$$m_v = \frac{6}{15 - 5} = \frac{3}{5}$$

The design determinant becomes:

$$\begin{vmatrix} 0 & \frac{3}{4}u & 1 \\ 1 & \frac{3}{5}v & 1 \\ \frac{5}{9} & \frac{1}{3}w & 1 \end{vmatrix} = 0 ,$$

The chart is constructed from this determinant (Figure 88). It should be noted that the u and v scales are graduated from points 2

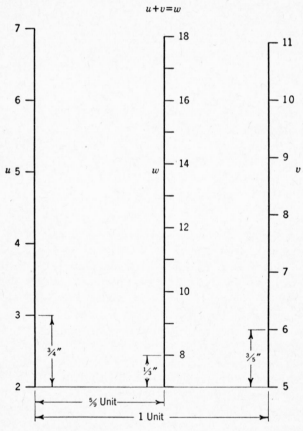

Fig. 88. Chart for the Equation, $u + v = w$, Constructed by the Method of Determinants.

and 5 respectively. A point on the w scale is obtained from the relation $u + v = w$.

GENERAL REMARKS

1. An equation which can be reduced to the determinant,

$$\begin{vmatrix} 0 & f_1(u) & 1 \\ f_2(v) & f_3(v) & 1 \\ f_4(w) & f_5(w) & 1 \end{vmatrix} = 0$$

will consist of a straight line u scale; and curved scales for v and w.

2. If the determinant is of the form:

$$\begin{vmatrix} f_1(u) & f_2(u) & 1 \\ f_3(v) & f_4(v) & 1 \\ f_5(w) & f_6(w) & 1 \end{vmatrix} = 0$$

the alignment chart will consist of three curved scales.

3. Design determinants of the form:

$$\begin{vmatrix} 0 & f_1(u) & 1 \\ 1 & f_2(v) & 1 \\ f_3(w) & 0 & 1 \end{vmatrix} = 0$$

will result in a chart having two parallel scales (u and v) and a transverse line for scale w.

The reduction of a given equation to the design determinant form frequently requires ingenuity and resourcefulness on the part of the designer. As one develops facility in manipulating determinants he will evolve short-cuts that will save much time.

In most cases the geometric method will be adequate for the design of alignment charts. However, complicated expressions, especially those which result in charts having two or three curves, may be solved more easily if the equation can be expressed in determinant form directly.

Projective transformations can be handled very nicely if the determinant forms are employed. The interested student is encouraged to consult the bibliography for a selection of books which stress the method of the determinants.

BIBLIOGRAPHY

The following list of books on nomography provides adequate reading for those who are interested in further study of the subject.

Encyclopédie des Sciences Mathématiques, Tome I, Vol. 4, Gauthier-Villars, Paris, 1908.

M. D'OCAGNE, *Traité de Nomographie*, 2nd Ed., Gauthier-Villars, Paris, 1921.

R. SOREAU, *Nomographie*, 2nd Ed., 2 Vols., Chiron, Paris, 1921.

P. WERKMEISTER, *Das Entwerfen, von graphischen Rechentafeln*, J. Springer, Berlin, 1923.

H. SCHWERDT, *Lehrbuch der Nomgraphie*, J. Springer, Berlin, 1924.

JOHN B. PEDDLE, *The Construction of Graphical Charts*, McGraw-Hill Book Co., New York, 1910.

CARL RUNGE, *Graphical Methods*, Lemcke and Buechner, New York, 1912.

JOSEPH LIPKA, *Graphical and Mechanical Computation*, John Wiley and Sons, New York, 1918.

S. BRODETSKY, *First Course in Nomography*, G. Bell and Sons, London, 1920, 2nd Ed., 1925.

W. N. ROSE, *Line Charts for Engineers*, E. P. Dutton and Co., New York, 1923.

L. I. HEWES and H. L. SEWARD, *Design of Diagrams for Engineering Formulas*, McGraw-Hill Book Co., New York, 1923.

W. J. KEARTON and GEORGE WOOD, *Alignment Charts for Engineers and Students*, J. B. Lippincott Co., Philadelphia, 1924.

G. W. SWETT, *Construction of Alignment Charts*, John Wiley and Sons, New York, 1928.

H. J. ALLCOCK and J. R. JONES, *The Nomogram*, Pitman Publishing Corp., New York, 1932.

C. O. MACKEY, *Graphical Solutions*, 2nd Ed., John Wiley and Sons, New York, 1936.

F. T. MAVIS, *The Construction of Nomographic Charts*, International Textbook Co., Scranton, Pa., 1939.

D. S. DAVIS, *Empirical Equations and Nomography*, McGraw-Hill Book Co., New York, 1943.

M. KRAITCHIK, *Alignment Charts*, D. Van Nostrand Co., New York, 1944.

INDEX TO APPENDIX ALIGNMENT CHARTS

APPENDIX

These are examples of alignment charts which may prove useful in the fields of engineering, production, business, and statistics.

$$E = \frac{336 \times R \times S}{D}$$

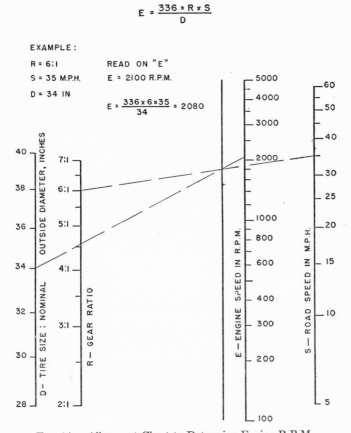

EXAMPLE:

R = 6:1

S = 35 M.P.H.

D = 34 IN

READ ON "E"

E = 2100 R.P.M.

$$E = \frac{336 \times 6 \times 35}{34} = 2080$$

FIG. 1A. Alignment Chart to Determine Engine R.P.M.

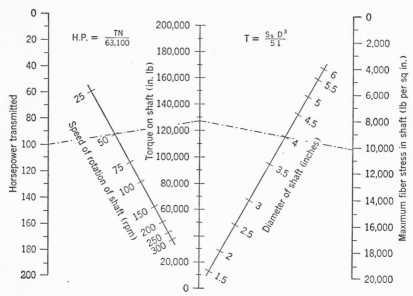

FIG. 2A.   Shafts for Torsional Strength.   (Courtesy *Product Engineering*.)

For calculating the horsepower that can be transmitted by a given shaft at a given speed, the follow ing equation can be used:

$$HP = \frac{S_s D^3 N}{322,000} \qquad (1)$$

This equation may be divided into two parts:

$$S_s = \frac{16T}{\pi D^3} \qquad (2)$$

and

$$HP = \frac{TN}{63,100} \qquad (3)$$

S_s = unit shearing stress,

D = diameter,

N = rpm,

and

T = torque.

Manipulation of the chart is illustrated by the dash lines.   Thus, if 100 hp is to be transmitted at a speed of 50 rpm, the stress in the outer fibers of a 4-in. diam. solid shaft will be slightly in excess of 10,000 lb per sq in.

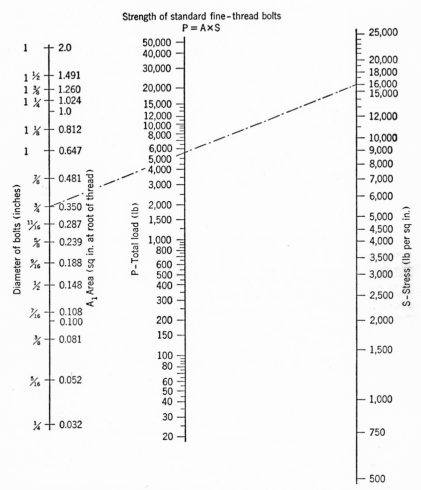

FIG. 3A. Strength of American Standard Bolts. (Courtesy *Product Engineering.*)

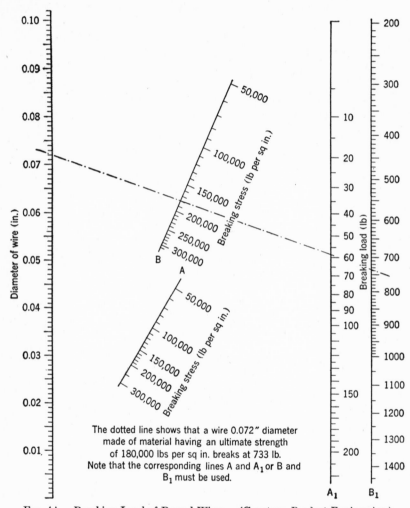

The dotted line shows that a wire 0.072″ diameter
made of material having an ultimate strength
of 180,000 lbs per sq in. breaks at 733 lb.
Note that the corresponding lines A and A₁ or B and
B₁ must be used.

FIG. 4A.   Breaking Load of Round Wires.   (Courtesy *Product Engineering*.)

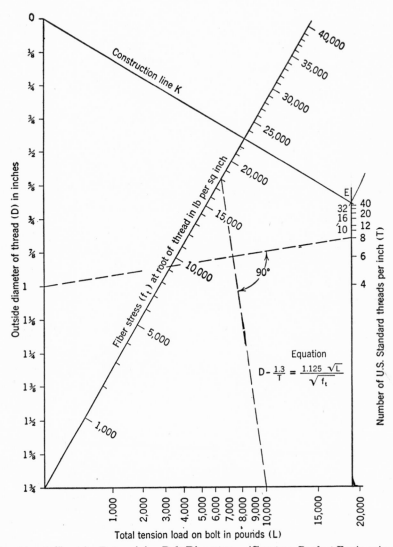

FIG. 5A. A Chart for Determining Bolt Diameters. (Courtesy *Product Engineering*.)

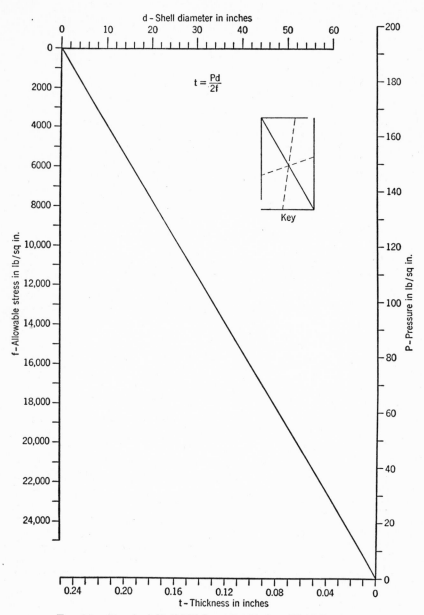

Fᴵɢ. 6A.   Required Shell Thickness for Various Fluid Pressures.

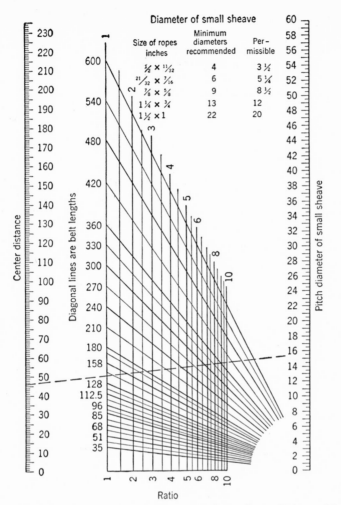

FIG. 7A. Chart for Finding Belt Lengths, V-Belt Short-Center Drives. (Courtesy *Product Engineering*. Information courtesy of Allis-Chalmers Manufacturing Co.)

Given pitch diameter of the small sheave, center distance, and speed ratio: to find length of V-belt, place straightedge on the given points of small sheave diameter (right) and center distance (left) and note intersection with ratio line (middle). Interpolate between diagonal belt length lines to obtain desired length.

EXAMPLE: Dotted line drawn between points representing small sheave diameter of 15.65 in. and center distance 46 in. intersects ratio line 2.6 at diagonal line for 180 in. belt length.

The V-belt drive consists of a driving and driven sheave, grooved for a multiplicity of belts of trapezoidal cross-section. Power is transmitted by the wedging contact between the belts and grooves. At maximum load, repeated tests show an efficiency of 99 per cent and a coefficient of friction of 1.5. V-belt drives operate, therefore, with comparatively small tension on the slack side, without slippage and with little creep. In figuring loads, it is usually safe to take 1.5 times the torque to get the total belt pull. Manufacturer's ratings must be consulted for selection of number and size of belts for given load conditions.

A V-belt drive will usually be well proportioned when the center distance equals or is slightly greater than the large sheave diameter. On small ratios the sheaves may be operated so closely together that the sheaves almost touch each other. Maximum center distance on $\frac{1}{2}$-in. belts is 17 in., except on high ratios, where 25 in. is permissible.

In the accompanying chart, the sheave diameters are the pitch diameters, measured at the midpoint of the trapezoidal section of the belt when resting in the groove.

145

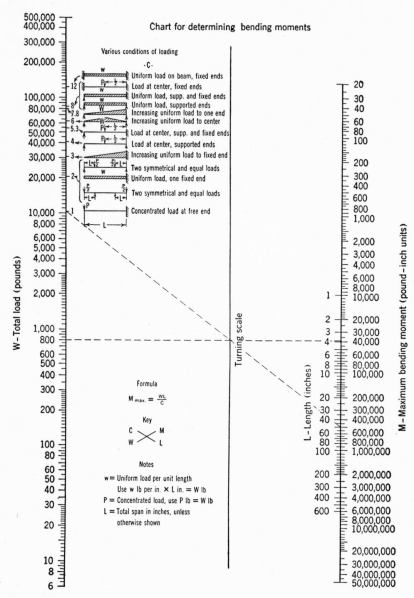

FIG. 8A. Chart for Determining Bending Moments. (Courtesy *Product Engineering*.)

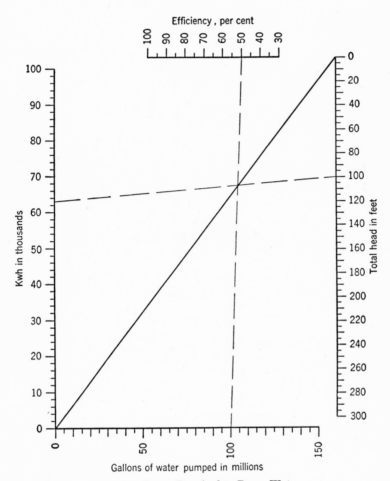

FIG. 9A. Power Required to Pump Water.

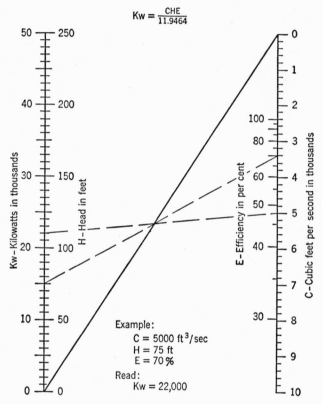

$$Kw = \frac{CHE}{11.9464}$$

Example:
C = 5000 ft³/sec
H = 75 ft
E = 70%
Read:
Kw = 22,000

FIG. 10A. Power Developed from Stream Flow.

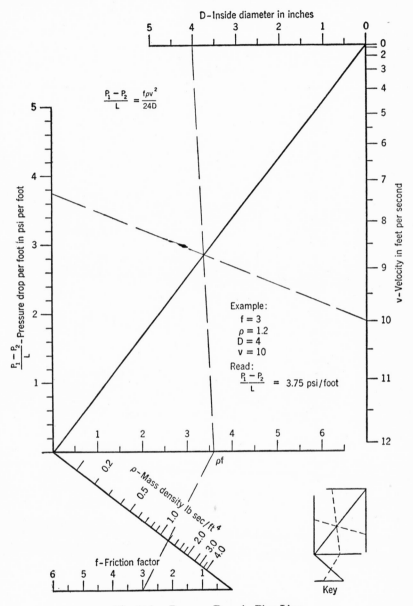

Fig. 11A. Pressure Drop in Pipe Line.

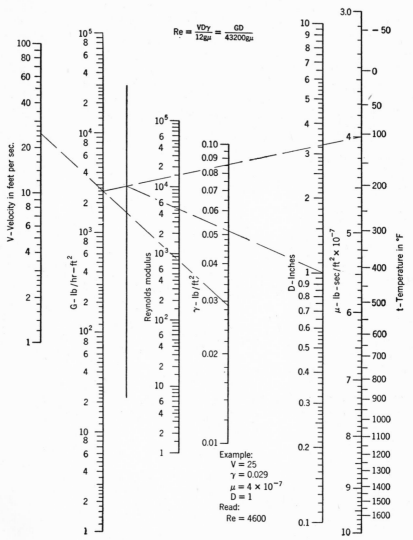

$$Re = \frac{VD\gamma}{12g\mu} = \frac{GD}{43200g\mu}$$

Example:
V = 25
γ = 0.029
μ = 4 × 10⁻⁷
D = 1
Read:
Re = 4600

FIG. 12A.   Reynolds Modulus for Air.

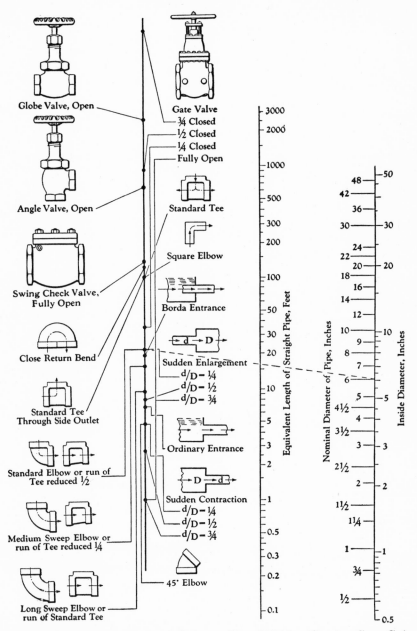

FIG. 13A   Resistance of Valves and Fittings to Flow of Fluids.   (Courtesy Crane Co.)

The chart on the page below solves the formula:

$$R_e = \frac{50.7 Q\rho}{d\mu} = \frac{35.5 B\rho}{d\mu} = \frac{6.32 W}{d\mu}$$

R_e = Reynolds number
Q = rate of flow, in gallons per minute
ρ = density of flowing fluid, in pounds per cubic foot
d = internal diameter of pipe, in inches
μ = absolute viscosity of fluid, in centipoise
B = rate of flow, in barrels per hour
W = rate of flow, in pounds per hour

Example: Oil is flowing through a 2-inch Standard new steel pipe at the rate of 600 barrels per hour. If the specific gravity of the oil is 0.97 and the viscosity at the flowing temperature is 14 centipoise, what is the Reynolds number and the friction factor?

Solution: Draw a line between 600 on the "B" scale and 0.97 on the "S" scale and mark the intersection of this line with the "W" scale. Connect this point with 2 on the nominal size scale and mark the intersection with the "μ" scale. Now draw a line from this point to 14 on the "μ" scale which intersects the "R_e" scale at 44,400. The Reynolds number is 44,400. Now draw a horizontal line from 44,400 on the "R_e" scale to the "R_e" line until this line intersects the friction factor curve for 2-inch pipe; now read the friction factor, .025, on the lower horizontal scale.

The friction factors of Pigott and Kemler for clean steel and wrought iron pipe are given on the chart.

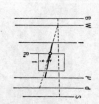

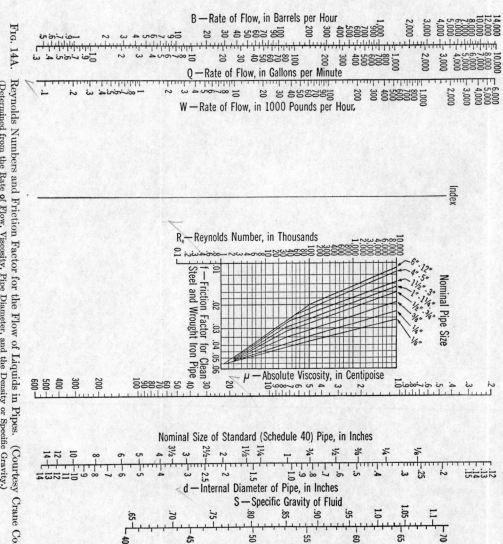

B — Rate of Flow, in Barrels per Hour
Q — Rate of Flow, in Gallons per Minute
W — Rate of Flow, in 1000 Pounds per Hour.

Index

R_e — Reynolds Number, in Thousands

Nominal Pipe Size

f — Friction Factor for Clean Steel and Wrought Iron Pipe

μ — Absolute Viscosity, in Centipoise

Nominal Size of Standard (Schedule 40) Pipe, in Inches

d — Internal Diameter of Pipe, in Inches
S — Specific Gravity of Fluid

ρ — Density of Fluid, in Pounds per Cubic Foot

FIG. 14A. Reynolds Numbers and Friction Factor for the Flow of Liquids in Pipes. (Courtesy Crane Co.)
(Determined from the Rate of Flow, Viscosity, Pipe Diameter, and the Density or Specific Gravity.)

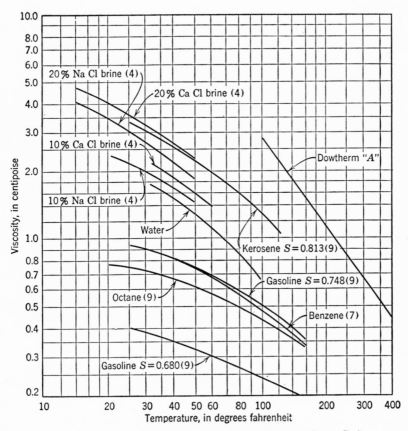

FIG. 15A.   Viscosity of Various Liquids.   (Courtesy Crane Co.)

It is good practice to assume that flow in pipes is turbulent for all Reynolds numbers greater than 1200. The chart on the page below is a solution of the Fanning formula for turbulent flow.

$$\Delta P_{100} = 0.129 \frac{f \rho v^2}{d} = 0.0215 \frac{f \rho Q^2}{d^5} = 0.0106 \frac{f \rho B^2}{d^5}$$

ΔP_{100} = pressure drop per 100 feet of pipe, in pounds per square inch

f = friction factor

ρ = density of flowing fluid, in pounds per cubic foot

v = mean velocity of flow, in feet per second

Q = rate of flow, in gallons per minute

B = rate of flow, in barrels per hour

d = internal diameter of pipe in inches

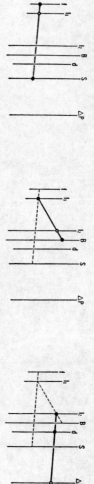

Example: Find the pressure drop in 250 feet of 6-inch Standard new steel pipe when handling gasoline at the rate of 600 barrels per hour. The specific gravity of the gasoline is 0.748 and the temperature is 60° Fahrenheit.

Solution: It is necessary to first determine the Reynolds number and the friction factor. From the graph (Figure 15A), the viscosity "μ" of 0.748 gravity gasoline is found to be 0.7 centipoise at 60° Fahrenheit. By using the chart, (Figure 14A), the Reynolds number is found to be 235,000 and

the friction factor .018. To find the pressure drop, connect 0.018 on the "f" scale, 0.748 on the "S" scale, and mark the intersection of this line with Index I. Draw a line between this point and 600 on the "B" scale and mark the intersection with Index II. Connect this point with 6.065 (inside diameter of 6-inch Standard pipe) on the "d" scale and extend the line to its intersection with the "ΔP_{100}" scale. The pressure drop is 0.39 pound per square inch per 100 feet of pipe or .39 × 2.5 = 0.975 pound per square inch for a length of 250 feet.

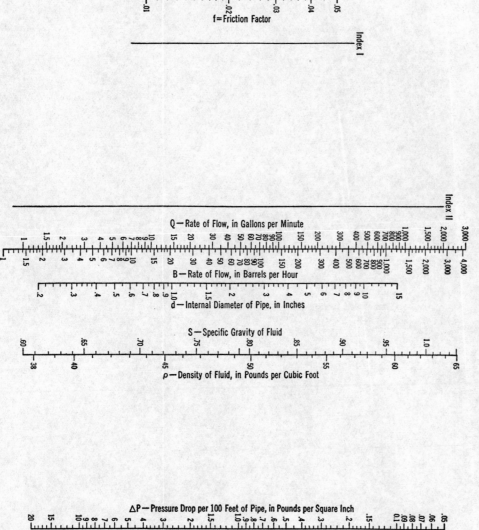

FIG. 16A.   Pressure Drop in Liquid Lines (Turbulent Flow).   (Courtesy Crane Co.)
(Determined from Rate of Flow, Friction Factor, Pipe Diameter, and Density.)

This chart is a graphical solution of the following equation:

$$q = \frac{A\sqrt{2gh}}{\sqrt{1.5 + f(L/D)}}$$

Using a friction factor of .018, this equation becomes:

$$Q = 19.5d^2 \sqrt{\frac{h}{1.5 + .018(L/D)}}$$

The location of the points on Scale C_d was determined from the equation:

$$Q = 450C_dA\sqrt{2gh}$$

Where:

q = discharge, in cubic feet per second
g = acceleration of gravity (32.2 feet per second per second)
h = static head, in feet of fluid
f = friction factor
L = length of pipe, in feet
D = internal diameter of pipe, in feet
d = internal diameter of pipe, in inches
C_d = coefficient of discharge
Q = discharge, in gallons per minute
A = orifice area, in square feet

Example: How much water will be discharged through a 1-inch sharp-edged orifice if the inlet head is 75 feet?

Solution: Connect 1 on the "d" scale with 75 on the "h" scale and mark the point of intersection with the index scale. Now connect this point with the arrowhead for sharp-edged orifice on Scale C_d; read the discharge on the "Q" scale. For the conditions of this problem, the discharge is 104 gallons per minute.

Values of $\frac{L}{D}$

Nominal Pipe Size Inches	Number of Pipe Diameters per 100 Ft. of Standard Pipe
⅛	4461
¼	3297
⅜	2434
½	1929
¾	1456
1	1144
1¼	869.6
1½	745.3
2	580.6
2½	486.0
3	391.1
4	298.1
5	237.8
6	197.9

Example: How much water will be discharged through 100 feet of 2-inch Standard pipe when the inlet head is 20 feet?

Solution: The inside diameter of 2-inch Standard pipe is 2.067 inches. The length in pipe diameters is:

$$\frac{L}{D} = \frac{12(100)}{2.067} = 580.6$$

Connect 2.067 on the "d" scale with 20 on the "h" scale and mark the intersection of this line with the index scale. Now connect this point with 580.6 on the "L/D" scale and read the discharge on the "Q" scale. The discharge is 106 gallons per minute.

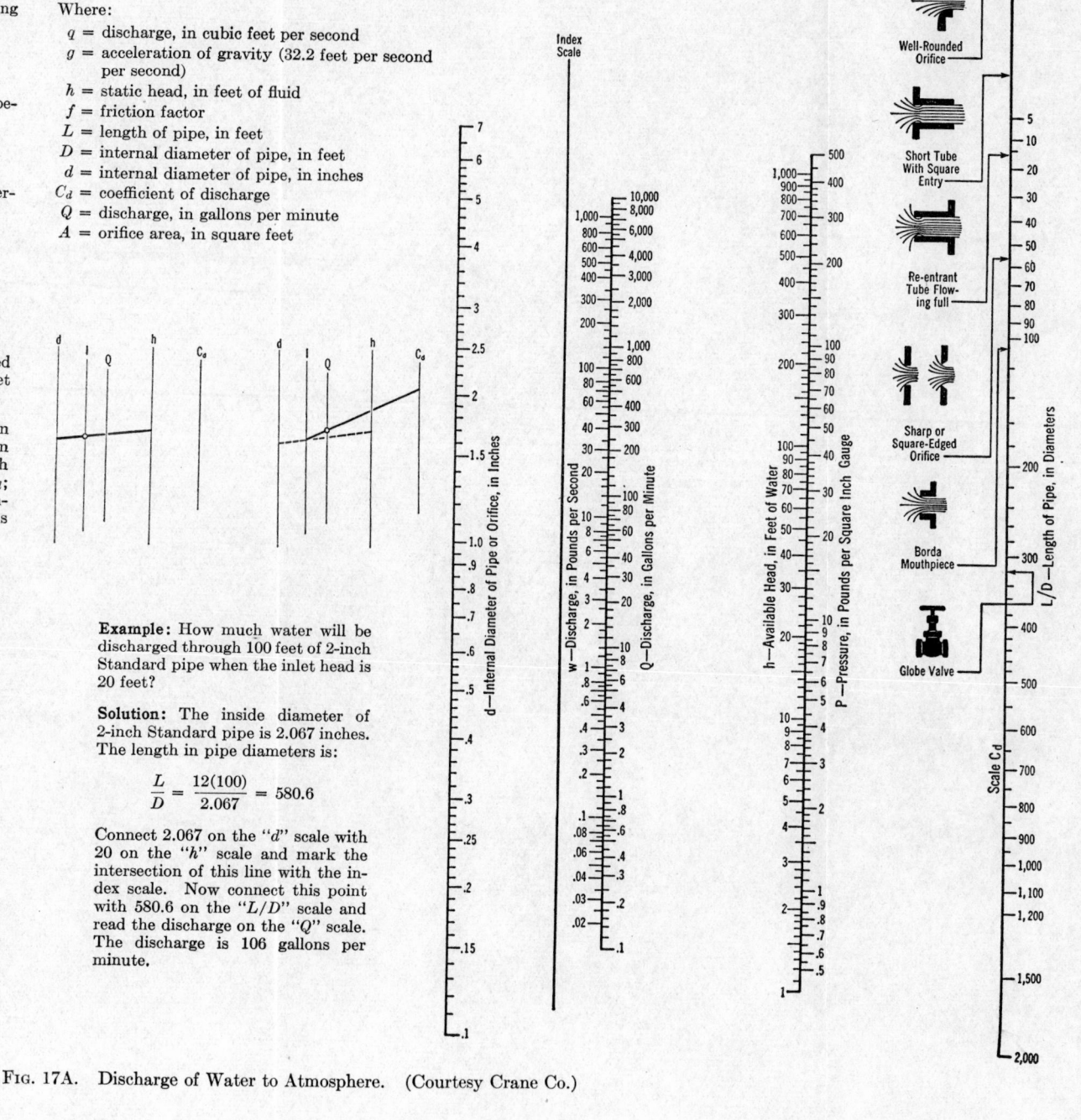

FIG. 17A. Discharge of Water to Atmosphere. (Courtesy Crane Co.)

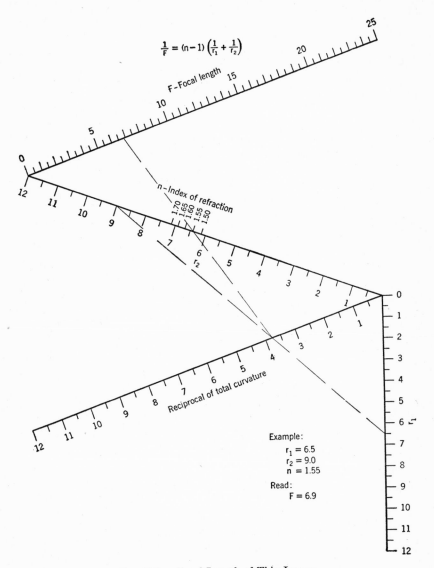

FIG. 18A. Focal Length of Thin Lenses.

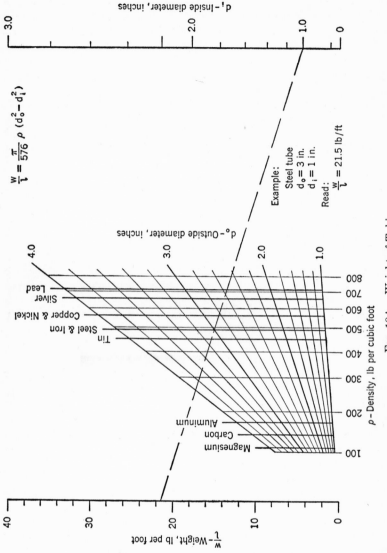

FIG. 19A. Weight of Tubing.

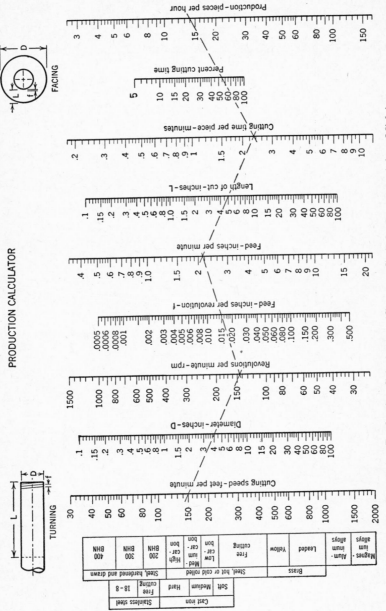

Fig. 20A. Production Calculator. (Courtesy Crobalt, Inc., Ann Arbor, Mich.)

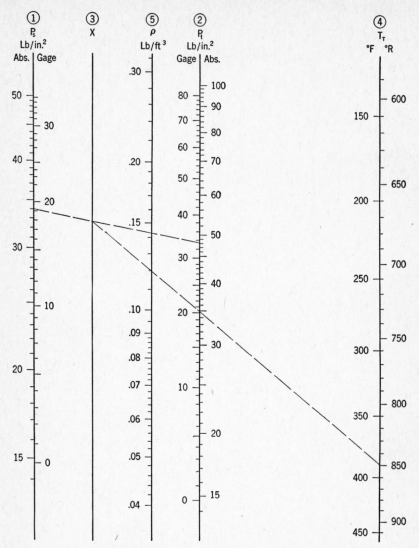

FIG. 21A.   Nomogram for Solving for Density of Fluid in a Pitot Tube Traverse.
(Courtesy Consolidated Vultee Aircraft Corp.)

$$\rho = \frac{P_S}{R} \times \frac{1}{T_T} \times \left(\frac{P_T}{P_S}\right)^{\frac{K-1}{K}}, \text{lb/ft}^3$$

$$K = 1.4 \text{ (for air)}$$

where R = 53.3 ft-lb/°F/lb of air

T_T = stagnation temp., °R

P_T = stagnation pres. $\Big\}$ similar units
P_S = static pres.

Example.   Given: P_S = 34.0 lb/in.² abs., P_T = 48.0 lb/in.² abs., T_T = 850°R.

Connect 34.0 on scale 1 to 48.0 on scale 2 and thus locate point X on scale 3.   Connect point X with 850 on scale 4 and read answer, ρ = 0.1195, on scale 5.

164

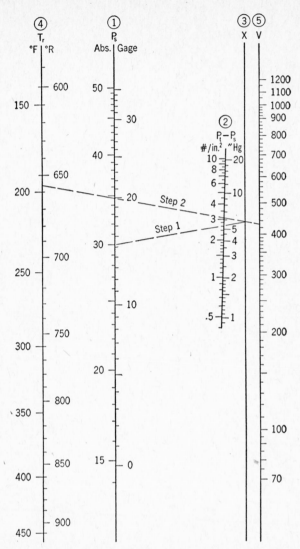

FIG. 22A. Nomogram for Solving the Pitot Tube Formula for Compressible Fluids. (Courtesy Consolidated Vultee Aircraft Corp.)

$$V = \sqrt{2gJC_PT_T \left[1 - \left(\frac{P_S}{P_T} \right)^{\frac{K-J}{K}} \right]} \text{ ft/sec}$$

where $g = 32.17$ ft/sec^2, $J = 778$ ft-lb/BTU, $K = 1.4$, $C_P = 0.24$ BTU/°F/lb air

T_T = stagnation temp., °R

P_T = stagnation pres. $\Big\}$ lb/in.^{2} abs. or similar units
P_S = static pres.

Example. Given: $P_S = 30.0$ lb/in.^{2} abs., $P_T - P_S = 2.6$ lb/in.^{2}, $T_T = 196$°F.

Connect 30.0 on scale 1 to 2.6 on scale 2 and note point X on scale 3. Connect this point with 196 on scale 4 and read answer on scale 5, $V = 429$ ft/sec.

165

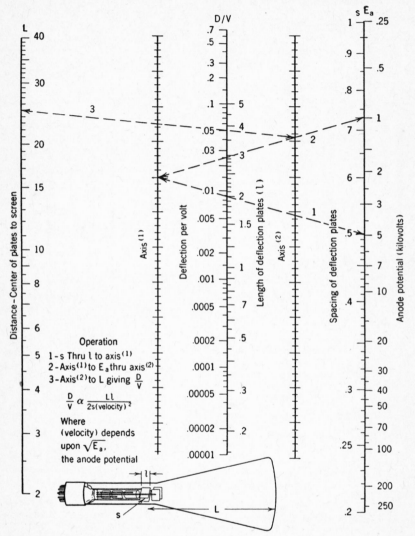

FIG. 23A. Deflection Sensitivity of Cathode Ray Tube—Electrostatic Deflection.
(Courtesy Federal Telephone and Radio Corp.)

The electrostatic deflection sensitivity of a cathode ray tube, for a given anode potential (E_a), depends on spacing (S) and length (l) of deflection plates, and their distance (L) to the screen. A line from (l) and (S) scales is extended to axis (1). From latter intersection a second line is drawn to (E_a) scale intersecting axis (2). From this point, a third line is drawn through (L) and extended to intersect D/V scale at left. (S), (l), (L), and (D) may all be in any convenient system of dimensions.

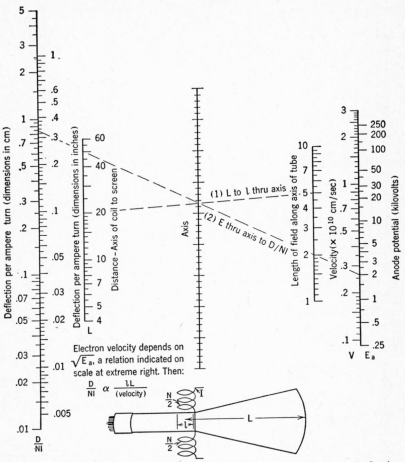

FIG. 24A. Deflection Sensitivity of Cathode Ray Tube—Electromagnetic Deflection. (Courtesy Federal Telephone and Radio Corp.)

The electromagnetic deflection sensitivity of a cathode ray tube cannot be determined with accuracy owing to difficulty of computing intensity and dimensions of magnetic field. With no flux leakage $H = .04\pi NI$, and the approximate deflection can be determined from chart, as indicated. The deflection per ampere turn scales (for use when dimensional systems are in centimeters and in inches) are at left. The scale at right shows electron velocity resulting from a given anode potential.

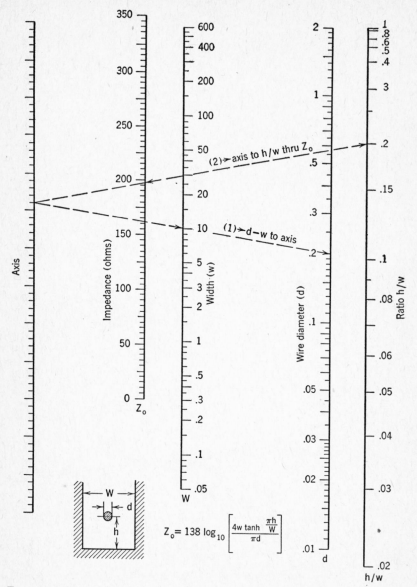

FIG. 25A. Characteristic Impedance of Lines—Single Wire in Trough. (Courtesy Federal Telephone and Radio Corp.)

Start with d and W values and extend line to axis. From latter point, a line to h/w scale will intersect Z_0 axis at resulting impedance value. Engineering accuracy when $w/d > 5$ and $h/d > 1.5$. Relations are only approximate beyond these values. Assumes lossless dielectric (air) and perfect conductors. Sides of trough assumed to extend to infinity. Any dimensional unit may be used. For other dielectrics multiply Z_0 by $1/\sqrt{\epsilon}$ where ϵ is dielectric constant.

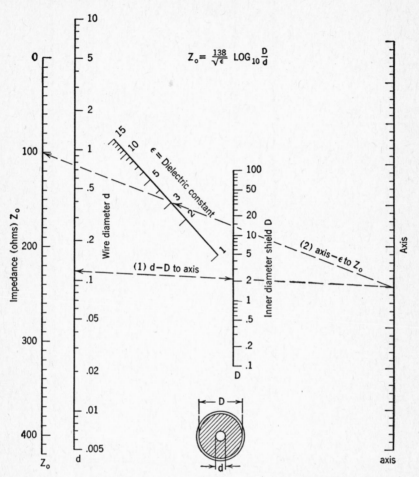

FIG. 26A.   Characteristic Impedance of Lines—Concentric Line, Solid Dielectric.
(Courtesy Federal Telephone and Radio Corp.)

This chart gives theoretically exact values for any scale of dimensions, if lossless dielectric is assumed (filling completely the space between conductors), and perfect conductors. Line from d and D scales extends to the axis. From latter point a line through E scale will intersect Z_0 scale at resulting value.

Example: $d = .12$ cm, $D = 2.1$ cm, $E = 3.0$, $Z_0 = 102$ ohms.

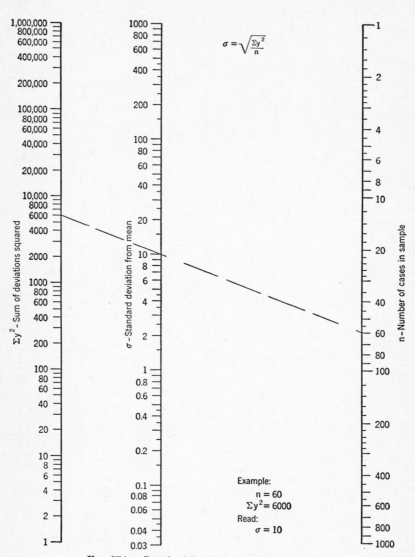

FIG. 27A.   Standard Deviation of a Set of Scores.

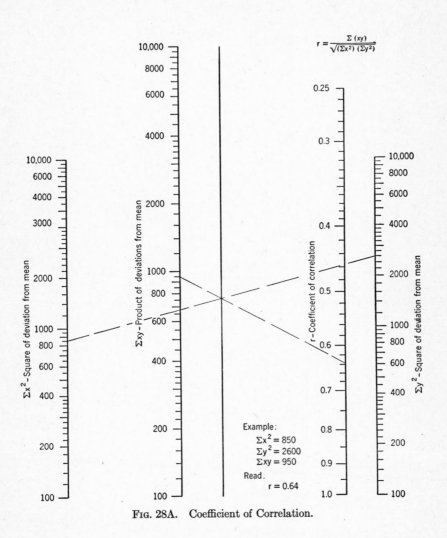

Fig. 28A.   Coefficient of Correlation.

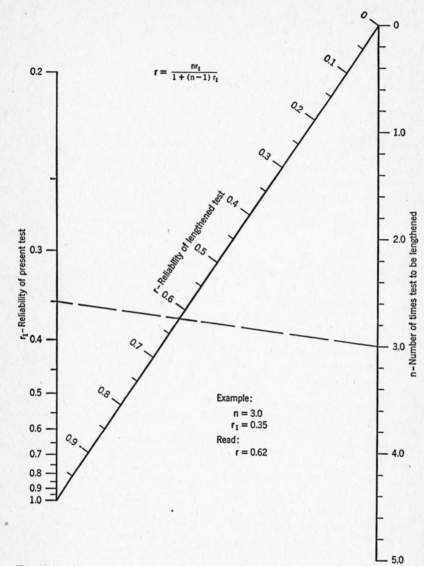

$$r = \frac{nr_{I}}{1 + (n-1)\, r_{I}}$$

r_I - Reliability of present test

r - Reliability of lengthened test

n - Number of times test to be lengthened

Example:
n = 3.0
r_I = 0.35
Read:
r = 0.62

FIG. 29A.   Spearman-Brown Prophecy Formula for Reliability of Lengthened Test.

INDEX

173